COPYRIGHT NOTE

CONTENTS

PUBLISHERS

Plan-A-Home
Lower Main Street,
Letterkenny, Co. Donegal.

BOOK MAKE UP & COMPUTER GRAPHICS

InCADessence
Computer Graphics Bureau
Office 8b, The Courtyard,
Lower Main St.
Letterkenny, Co. Donegal.

PRINTERS

Universities Press
Alanbrooke Road,
Belfast.

ACKNOWLEDGEMENTS

Designs:
Clifford Glean
Gavin Clinch
Adam Leadley
Harold McGuinness
Manus Ferry
Paul Cassidy
Attracta Winters

Editorials:
Adam Leadley
Liam Cotter
Clifford Glean
Harold McGuinness
Attracta Winters

InCADessence:
Gavin Clinch

Contributors:
Seamus McTague

THE PLAN-A-HOME SERVICE:
FOR THE PROVISION OF UNALTERED PLANS

A simple and economical means of obtaining high quality plans and contract specification documents.
All plans are prepared to:

A high quality of design and presentation.

Comply with current Building Regulations.

Include your own specific choices of materials and finishes.

Please be sure that your chosen plans suit your needs. If you are uncertain about anything you should obtain professional advice before ordering. For plans requiring alterations and for customised designs see page 5.
It should be noted that some of the more elaborate designs in this book are not available via mail and are purely illustrations of theoretical design.

TO ORDER YOUR PLANS

LoCALL 1890 222345
or 00 353 74 29651 (outside Eire)
for the cost of your plans.

* THEN *

FILL out the forms on pages <u>143 & 144</u>

This service is ONLY available through PLAN-A-HOME.
Please allow up to 15 working days for delivery.

THE FULL ARCHITECTURAL SERVICE:
FOR CUSTOMISED DESIGNS

HMG Associates, Architects.   **PAH Associates, Architects.**

See inside back cover for office details and locations.

All of the following services are provided by HMG Associates throughout Ireland, and by PAH Associates in Cork. These architects retain the sole franchise from PLAN-A-HOME to work and alter any Plan-A-Home design to suit client needs.

Site Analysis and Survey

This is most important in ascertaining the house style to best suit your site and needs. Design style, proper aspect, best views, creating best impression at entrance to site, relationship to adjoining structures, planning constraints are some of the many concerns. Other information in relation to preparation of site maps for planning and tendering is observed and recorded on site.

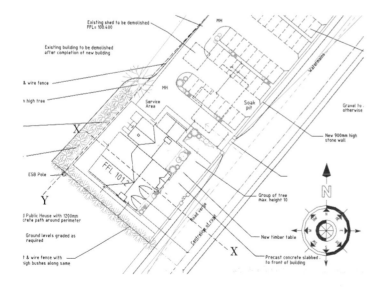

Design Consultation

Comprehensive discussions are required to determine your needs in order to prepare the initial sketch layouts. You may wish to bring the following to any design meeting: a personalised wish list; this should include initial design brief ideas, special requirements, budget and any other relevant material. From here we can, in simple steps, work towards an agreed final design.

Planning Permission

Preparations and submissions of all drawings, documents and notices required for planning applications. Liaison with the local planning authority should any difficulties arise during your application.

Working Drawings

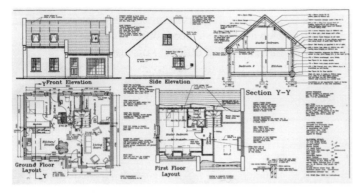

These are prepared after agreement has been reached on design sketches. Naturally some flexibility for change is still possible as final drawings near completion. Working drawings and specifications are to a standard that building contractors are fully aware of all details and finishes required, both for tendering and construction purposes, therefore eliminating unforeseen extras.

Tendering Procedures

A list of builders to tender is normally drawn up by agreement between the Architect and client. Tender analysis i.e. thorough scrutiny of tenders, is fundamental to the successful awarding of any contract.

Quantity Surveying

Prior to finalising any design we strongly recommend that you avail of our Quantity Surveying Service. This runs in parallel with our Architectural service to establish construction costs and to highlight any design adjustments necessary to suit specific budgets. Having your scheme costs in advance is very useful when evaluating tender prices and budgeting for interim payments.

Supervision

Supervision of any project is highly recommended as the unsuspecting client can easily be caught out by contractual loopholes and the unscrupulous builder. Supervision involves constant liaison with contractors, client and other members of the design team to achieve the best results and make certain that all efforts expended during design are strictly enforced. We ensure that all works and finishes are up to the highest standard and in compliance with Building Regulations, Planning and Mortgage Requirements. In essence this service removes responsibility and liability for those who are in the process of building.

Structural Inspections

If full supervision is not required, structural inspections are advisable and indeed a prerequisite for most mortgage companies. This involves:-
i)   inspection of open foundation trenches.
ii) inspection of preparation of concrete ground floors.
iii) inspection of all roofing timbers and structures.
iv) inspection at practical completion.

■   These services would be included within the full supervision package.

Commercial/Industrial

With professional teams of architectural staff both HMG Associates and PAH Associates handle all types of projects, from design to planning, tendering and supervision.
This service is backed up with state of the art computerised drawing offices offering both flexibility in design and photo-realistic images.

Projects to date include:

Industrial -   **Fish processing plants**
                Storage & retail units
                Fish handling units.
Commercial - **Shopping units**
                Filling stations
                Bars, lounges & restaurants
                Tourism projects.

Housing Schemes

We offer a comprehensive service to potential developers, naturally as each developers' needs differ we tailor the service to suit. Call into any of our offices to discuss your requirements. Office locations are given inside back cover.

The Service includes:

Preliminary investigations, site suitability and analysis, full survey.
Design concepts for housing and site.
Working drawings, site layout, services drawings.
Bill of Quantities, all relevant cost projections.
Tailored supervision requirements.
3-Dimensional computer modelling.

CHOOSING THE SITE

Everyone building a new home has a responsibility to ensure that the development, not only meets their requirements but is also responsive and sensitive to the landscape and surrounding countryside. As no two sites are the same it is important to recognise and design for the individual character of the site. Your Architect is the best person to consult with and this should be done prior to deciding on your own design. The trend today is to clear a site, prior to construction, though total site clearance can be detrimental to the character of your site. This is not necessary in order to construct your house. In many cases it is best to retain some of the existing features, e.g. trees, hedgerows and mounds to retain the appeal of the original site.

Main design considerations

Aspect

It's important that your living spaces should avail of the natural path of the sun, to gain maximum light and warmth. Prioritising these to the southern and western sides is the ideal solution but often other site restrictions may re-prioritise the final orientation of the rooms. The final shape of the footprint of your house will determine how successful this can be achieved. Your Architect should be the best person to assist you on this matter

View

If your site has a view, often compromise is required to maximise view and sunlight. For example a northern view may require a style of design so as to bring the light in from another direction. This need not necessarily mean a more complicated or expensive design but simply a well though out design taking into account all available features and aspects.

Access

Access should have two main considerations.
Firstly a sensible access to the public road both from a planning requirement and safety view point. Adequate sight lines must be established in order to prove that safe access onto the road can be achieved.

Secondly, the initial impression of your house on the approach driveway may be the most important, and in most cases would clearly show the main entrance door so as to ensure that guests enter the house in the manner in which it was intended. In some cases this can mean the main front door located on what might realistically be the rear of the house. In such cases the rear would require additional treatment so as to give it more of a welcoming appeal.

Should you have a definite style of house you require, then contact your Architect prior to purchasing your site as there are many aspects about your site that will dictate the type of house best suited to it.

In many cases the client has agreed on the site prior to discussing designs an often this choice is governed by:

1. Location
This will obviously be a very personal choice and is quite often influenced by surroundings, view, convenience to amenities and family.

2. Cost
This is a much more complex issue whereby the purchase price of a site with disadvantages is not necessarily a true reflection and would require more expenditure in bringing the site up to a suitable standard. Check for the following when purchasing a site.

(a) Electricity
Each additional pole required to reach your site costs extra money.

(b) Water
A well would cost at least £1000 more than connecting to mains water.

(c) Sewage
Adjacent mains sewage, if available, or a septic tank are the economical options, however ground conditions may require a sewage treatment solution which will incur an additional £2000 to £4000

(d) Levels

A low lying site can incur substantial extra cost in
> Additional dead blockwork
> Filling to bring up floor levels
> Filling to bring up drive, paths and general site areas

An overly elevated site can cost extra in
> Extra excavation and carting same off site
> Possible rock excavation

(e) Ground conditions
Poor ground condition usually cause unforseen expence both in foundation design, hardcore filling and any other ancillary siteworks or structures.

(f) Boundaries
A site with natural boundaries will obviously avoid the additional cost of providing new boundaries which can in most instances be more expensive than anticipated

Kingspan Insulation offer a complete **Therma** solution to all domestic applications

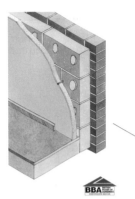

Kingspan Therma*wall* *TW52*
Insulation/plasterboard composite wall lining
for use in internal drylining applications.
Can also be fixed to timber framing/battens.

Kingspan Therma*wall* *TW50*
A partial fill foil faced cavity wall insulation
board for use in traditional cavity wall
insulation.

Kingspan **Kool**therm *K7/*
Kingspan **Therma***pitch TP10*
Insulated sarking boards for
installation over the rafters in
pitched roof construction.

Can also be used:
- between rafters
- between and beneath rafters

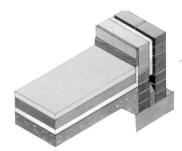

Kingspan Therma*floor TF70*
A high performance insulation board for use in solid
and suspended floor construction.

Kingspan Therma*deck TD31*
Insulation/exterior grade plywood composite roof
decking for flat roofing applications.

Kingspan **Therma***roof TR21* is also available for
partially bonded built-up felt flat roofing applications.

Kingspan Insulation

Kingspan Insulation offers the widest range of insulants available from any Irish manufacturer, which all stacks up to a better Insulation Solution.

The Kooltherm K-Range is the premium performance insulant with the lowest lambda value of any commonly used insulant on the Irish market. Its phenolic insulation composition can offer fire performance and smoke emission comparable with mineral fibre, with no significant moisture absorption.

The Therma range of high performance rigid urethane insulation offers low lambda values with negligible moisture absorption, and a product for every application.

Styrodur high performance xps insulation has a high compression strength and negligible moisture absorption making it ideal for many specialist building applications. Add to this, back up from the technical service department of one of Ireland's largest non-fibrous insulation board manufacturers, and you'll see why Kingspan Insulation Solutions make sense.

When it comes to designing or building your own home, one essential consideration must be how to make the most effective use of the available roofspace.

There's little comfort in wasting unused, valuable, living space. Space that can, with a little imagination, contribute so much more to enriching the quality of the environment we live in. Traditionally, the roofspace above bedroom ceiling height is effectively a cold and damp storage space, which houses the cold water tank and is one of the greatest risk areas for freezing pipes.

Simply by using Kingspan Kooltherm K-7 or Thermapitch TP I 0 insulated sarking boards to provide a warm pitched roof, instead of using conventional mineral fibre loft insulation between the joists of a cold roof construction, means that wasted, lifeless, attic space can be easily transformed into a living area with space, light and air to create a unique atmosphere.

Insulating at rafter level, rather than at the traditional ceiling level has numerous benefits:-

- It creates, on average, 15% more usable living or storage space.
- It increases the value of a property.
- There is no risk of condensation in the roof area.
- It eliminates the need for a vapour control layer, with the inclusion of a breathable membrane above the insulation
- It eliminates the need for cross ventilation.
- It eliminates the need for lagging of pipes and tanks.

Rigid insulation is particularly suited to this application, it's key benefit being it's outstanding thermal efficiency, which derives from the core's unique closed cell structure. This means that far less material is needed to achieve the required thermal performance. The thickness of Kingspan products required to achieve a give 'U'-value is considerably less than other insulants such as polystyrene or mineral fibre.

When it comes to insulating external walls, Kingspan can provide the ideal solutions, Kingspan Thermawall TW52, a high performance rigid insulation/plasterboard composite wall lining for use in internal drylining applications, or Kingspan Thermawall TW50, a high performance foil faced rigid partial fill cavity wall insulation, for use in traditional cavity wall construction.

Thermawall TW52 provides insulation and an internal wall finish in one product and is easily installed utilising standard drylining techniques. Insulating internally allows a traditional clear cavity to be maintained in cavity wall construction. Thermawall TW52 is available with insulation thicknesses of 20-50mm typically providing 'U'-Values in the range 0.54-0.30 W/m2K.

Thermawall TW50 maintains a clear cavity within the wall construction, which is the preferred option to prevent wind driven rain penetration through the wall, available in a raise of thicknesses providing 'U'-Values typically in the range 0.57-0.27 W/m2K.

Where performance matters, whether insulating roofs, walls or floors, you'll know that better Insulation Solutions come from Kingspan.

Keeragh

Cladding this cottage in stone may be a little extravagant but it does give great character. However, it would appear equally homely in a plain white render if preferred or budget demands.

Whilst the windows are not large their regularity will ensure good natural lighting to all rooms.

DIMENSIONS & AREAS

LIVING	16' 3" x 11' 6"
KITCHEN	13' 3" x 11' 2"
BED 1	13' 7" x 11' 10"
BED 2	10' 6" x 12' 4"
LENGTH	38' 5"
FLOOR AREA	925 sq. ft.

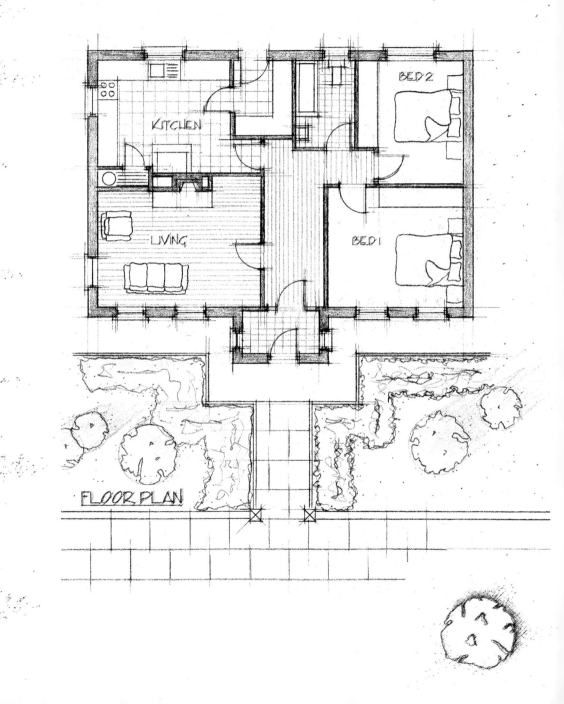

FLOOR PLAN

13

Inishfree

Thatch is undergoing something of a revival these days and its undoubted charm is perfect for a country cottage retreat.
The living area opens off the kitchen through sliding doors, creating one large room if desired or dictated by a large party of revellers.
The fuel store is accessed internally - a blessing if its blowing a hooley outside.

DIMENSIONS & AREAS

LIVING	13' 1" x 16' 5"
KITCHEN	16' 5" x 16' 5"
BED 1	9' 10" x 16' 5"
LENGTH	42' 8"
FLOOR AREA	860 sq. ft.

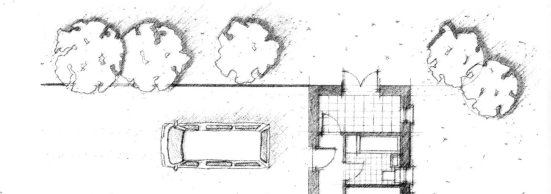

BED 1

KITCHEN

LIVING

FLOOR PLAN

Inishlachen

Sun lounges feature in many of the designs in this book. They are perhaps an added luxury to any house but one which could be considered essential to a holiday home. Here the juxtaposition of a modern fully glazed sun lounge to the traditional style cottage is seamless.

DIMENSIONS & AREAS

LIVING	16' 5" x 10' 6"
KITCHEN	16' 5" x 13' 5"
SUN LOUNGE	10' 3" x 10' 3"
BED 1	14' 10" x 12' 8"
BED 2	9' 8" x 12' 10"
LENGTH	50' 0"
FLOOR AREA	1052 sq. ft.

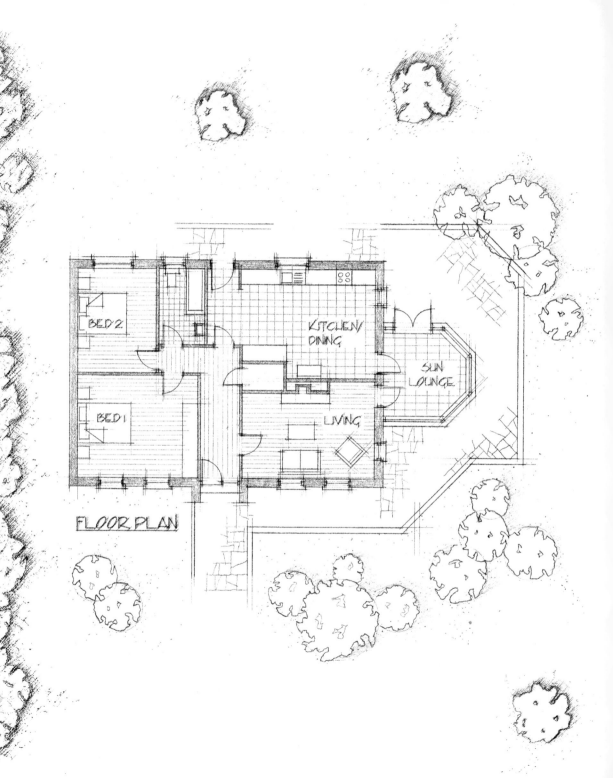

BED 2

KITCHEN/ DINING

SUN LOUNGE

BED 1

LIVING

FLOOR PLAN

Inishboffin

A traditional design that opens up internally from the kitchen, through dining, living, bedroom and finally patio, by way of large double doors.
Thus allowing the easy passage of a cooling breeze on a hot summers day. This type of floor plan would lend itself to a compact retirement cottage.

DIMENSIONS & AREAS

LIVING	17' 1" x 13' 4"
KITCHEN	12' 5" x 10' 0"
DINING	12' 5" x 11' 0"
BED 1	11' 0" x 13' 5"
BED 2	11' 0" x 12' 6"
BED 3	10' 6" x 8' 8"
LENGTH	43' 2"
FLOOR AREA	1080 sq. ft.

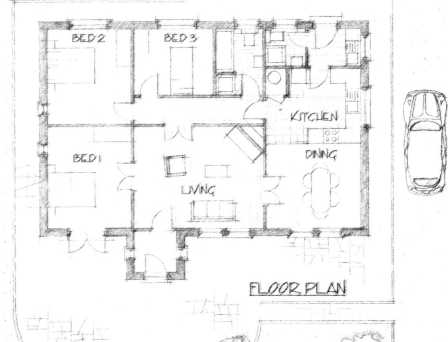

FLOOR PLAN

Craggy

A simple layout with living accomodation downstairs and sleeping above. this style of house is ideal for short holidays or weekend breaks. Sufficient storage space is provided for most recreational materials.
An external store or garage could easily be added to either gable end.
Use of bright colours externally add to the excitement of vaction time.

DIMENSIONS & AREAS

LIVING	15' 11" x 16' 5"
KITCHEN/DINING	12' 11" x 16' 5"
BED 1	11' 7" x 16' 5"
BED 2	13' 0" x 16' 5"
LENGTH	42' 8"
FLOOR AREA	1237 sq. ft.

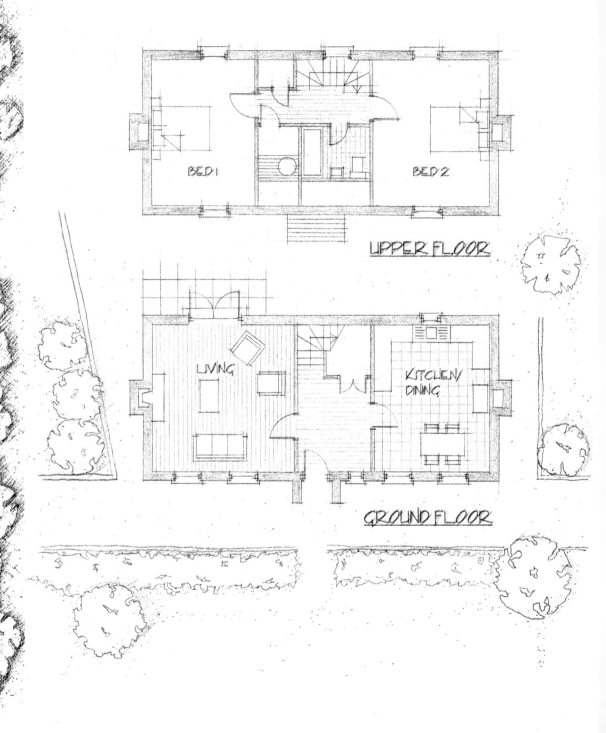

BED 1   BED 2

UPPER FLOOR

LIVING   KITCHEN/DINING

GROUND FLOOR

Rathlin

The open entrance hallway gives access to all ground floor rooms which are bright and naturally lit. The feature bay window in the lounge gives greater emphasis to the entrance elevation.

The two large bedrooms at first floor level are set within the roof space and delightfully lit giving a country cottage effect internally.

DIMENSIONS & AREAS

LIVING	15' 9" x 12' 6"
KITCHEN	10' 0" x 12' 0"
DINING	10' 8" x 12' 0"
BED 1	14' 8" x 12' 6"
BED 2	13' 1" x 12' 6"
LENGTH	40' 4"
FLOOR AREA	1484 sq. ft.

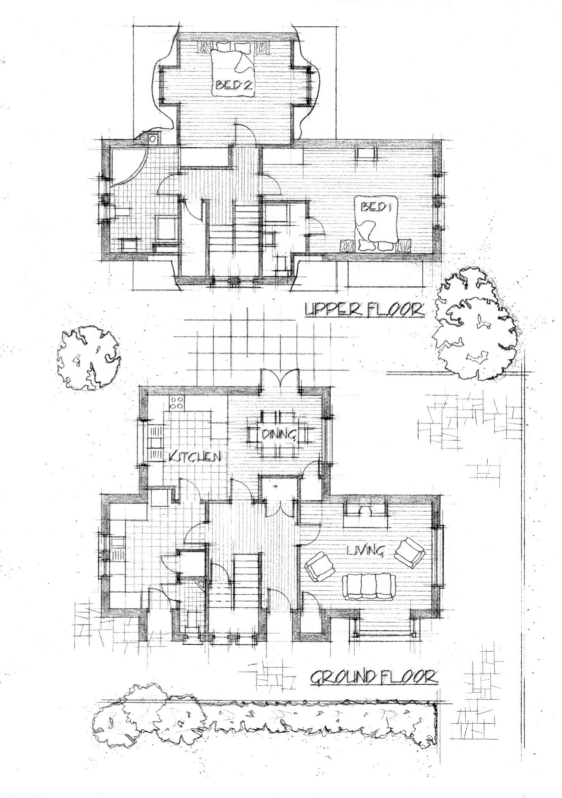

UPPER FLOOR

GROUND FLOOR

CREATING AN ENTRANCE

First impressions are crucial. The entrance, being the first experience of a house often generates an image of the house as a whole. Traditionally the larger scale of house the grander the doorway, giving increased emphasis on the entrance.

The doorway itself is important; a heavy door will create a sense of solidly whilst a partially or fully glazed door will give a feeling of openness and light.

The front doors of Ireland traditionally made a statement. Finished with a bright primary colour such as red or blue, they contrast boldly with the whitewashed walls. These entrances, though solid, were most welcoming with some being constructed as a "stable door" allowing the occupants to lean across the threshold and socialise whilst still retaining the privacy of being within the home.

When choosing a door be true to the building, avoid bevelled glass, columns and pressed woodgrain on metal or upvc, all look inauthentic . A simple hardwearing timber door such as oak, elm or teak looks far better than a door pretending to have been crafted 100 years ago.

HALLWAYS AND PORCHES

One of the main functions of a hall is to create an area between inside and out and provide a means of circulation to and from different areas within the house. As an entrance to your home it must be accessible to all users and visitors including parents with prams and people in wheelchairs.

In the smaller house getting rid of the entrance hall to enlarge the living area may seem a good idea, but stepping directly into the living room deprives the occupant of the opportunity to shake off the outside prior to entering proper into a house. The halfway point of a house is removed as a stranger at the door steps instantly into the heart of the home. A hallway acts as a breathing space and should be lit naturally wherever possible, creating a welcoming light warm area into which one feels comfortable in entering.

For smaller houses it is best to leave a hallway uncluttered with storage provided for coats and shoes, which leaves the through route clear. Even coat hooks, when fully loaded on a wall will give the space a claustrophobic feel.As an area of circulation, the hallway provides an opportunity to create something more than just a space to pass through. With the use of book shelving and pictures and perhaps a telephone and natural lighting it can become a powerful focus within the house. Its primary use however remains circulation and it should not become cluttered and impede your passage through the house which will cause annoyance and act as a potential safety hazard.

STAIRS

Often the hall serves as the main circulation space and in many two-storey homes the stair leads off the entrance hall. It is wise to maximise the natural lighting so decreasing the dependency on artificial light.

The staircase can generate one of the most dramatic focuses and should be treated as an active element within the house. It is the first thing visitors to the house see and is so often a missed opportunity. Traditionally a staircase was a means of travelling between floors in a building and was treated as such. A low-key affair often painted to blend in rather than stand out. More and more, a staircase is adding to the status of a property and with the enormous choice of materials now available, from traditional timber to contemporary steel and glass it is easy to create an image suited to the individual.

Whichever treatment you choose the level of lighting is important. Low levels of light are acceptable and safe providing there is a clear distinction between the risers and treads. Avoid spotlights shining into people's eyes and flat shadowless light, both reducing the definition of the risers.

By introducing views and windows along the flight the journey up and down can be made more enjoyable. Using the walls for hanging paintings and photographs all help to give the stair-case a sense of place.

KITCHENS & UTILITIES

The kitchen is one of the most important centres of a house. It is not just a functional workspace but an area in which a family can live and interact.

Over the last 100 years the kitchen has been regarded as a work room with little thought to anything beyond its function. An ever-increasing interest in the kitchen as a family room has seen the re-emergence of the traditional kitchen as more open plan incorporating a range and hearth.

When designing your own home the kitchen can be formulated to exact individual requirements. One of the most important steps is to decide what type of room and style of kitchen is required. If the kitchen is to be used as a social space it may be worthwhile spending time and money generating the correct spacial quality and light. Incorporating the dining room into the kitchen area can create an extra multi-functional space allowing interaction between working in the kitchen and activities within the adjoining space.

Careful planning of the kitchen is paramount to its success and ease of use. Everyone has their own individual requirements and priorities for kitchen design. There are however three primary functions; the washing area, the cooking area and the food storage. These will generate the fundamental layout of the kitchen. The relationship between these three functions is known as the work triangle, an imaginary line drawn between the three work centres. Each area must be clearly defined with clear passage from one area to another. The travel distances between the functions should be close enough as to not cause irritation from long travelling distances and far enough apart to avoid cramped movement.

Traditionally the sink was positioned in front of the window. It made sense to locate a function that can be time consuming next to a natural light source. This is not compulsory although it can feel odd facing a wall while using the sink. If a source of natural light is not available a more acceptable location would be facing out towards the room on an island or an outshot. Quality design is as much to do with being aesthetically pleasing as ensuring smooth performance. When it comes to kitchens and accessories it is essential to take a total approach. A kitchen can be destroyed by the discordant note of mismatched dimensions, non co-ordinated colours as ill-conceived variations in textures. Individual requirements must be studied and met in both terms of visual design and the performance and range of facilities available. With the amount of electrical appliances available it is easy to overload a kitchen with gadgets. All fitted appliances should be integrated into the overall design theme selected for the kitchen. Door panels identical or co-ordinated with the colour scheme and dimensions are often fitted to the appliance door, hiding an unattractive unit such as a dishwasher, although with today's designer appliances many choose to highlight the washing machine or dishwasher as part of the whole kitchen display.

With the advent of the utility room there is now a choice of location for the more bulky, noisy and visually unappealing items which would have normally been accommodated within the main kitchen area using up valuable storage space.

Offering a separate area where clothes can be washed, dried and ironed and all household cleaning equipment can be stored reinforces the identity of the kitchen as an integral part of the house. The utility acts as a rear porch from the outside keeping dirt and wet away from the kitchen. It offers the opportunity to remove coats and shoes before entering the main house.

A utility room should have easy clean surfaces for the floor, walls and units, a double or deep sink unit for handwashing clothes and space for the washing machine and tumble dryer. A drying rack either floor or ceiling mounted is a necessary accessory even if a tumble dryer is installed. A ceiling rack will save space.

The utility room is also an ideal location for boiler, freezers, the hot-press and the storage of household products such as shoe cleaning equipment and general household products. It is also the ideal location for a w.c. so eliminating the need to remove shoes or coats prior to entering the house.

The lifespan of a kitchen depends on the quality of the materials used, method of manufacture and the way it is fitted. As chipboard is the main ingredient, it is very important that it is of high quality and, more importantly, that it is machined and edged properly. All edges should be sealed with edging tape, even the ones that are not seen, as this prevents them absorbing moisture. Since most of the doors used by kitchen manufacturers are brought in from specialist door manufacturers, the quality is usually assured.

When buying a kitchen you should decide on how much money you have to spend and then shop around for the best buy. On finding one you like the following relevant questions should be asked.

Do the floor cabinets have legs on them?
Do they have a ledge to support the gable of the cabinet?
(It is very important that they have this ledge otherwise the floor to gable fitting is taking the whole weight).
Are the legs metal or plastic?
(Metal legs are stronger than plastic)
What guarantee is given and is it in writing?
Do they make the doors or are they bought in?
Do they stain and lacquer the door and endpanels themselves?
Are the panels melamine or real wood veneer?
(Veneer is best but more expensive).
Are the shelves adjustable and the longer ones supported in the centre to prevent sagging?
Does the worktop have a water safe edge?
Is the cornice and light pelmet solid timber or MDF?
(It should be solid).
What thickness is the chipboard in the carcase?
(This should not be less then 16mm, preferably 18mm).
What way are the cabinet doors put together are they KD fittings or wood dowels?
Is there a quality control system in stock?
Have their kitchens undergone independent testing?
(Check details).
When ordering materials do they specify the quality they require?
Do they check on the delivery of goods that they are up to the standard ordered?
Is there a contract form to be signed?
Don't let all these questions put your off. Any manufacturer who thinks quality will welcome them, even if they can't answer positively to them all. The answer to the first two questions should be yes, even on the cheapest kitchen you can buy. Check for yourself the thickness of the cupboard, the drawers, hinges and the shelf supports. Also, if the doors are solid timber, slide your fingers around the edges of the centre panel – this should be smooth to the touch. But most important, check out the person you are dealing with. Remember you can trade in your car if you are not happy with it; have a bad kitchen fitted and you are stuck with it.

DINING ROOMS

Eating should be a social activity and not just a re-fuelling process. The act of eating should be an enjoyable experience giving opportunity to socialise with family or friends. A relaxing occasion in a pleasant atmosphere.

The traditional "formal" dining room has lost popularity just as the kitchen has an ever-increasing positive focus. Unless you formally entertain on a regular basis a formal room designated purely for dining will be a waste of a room receiving only occasional usage.
Today's dining room is a multi-functional space located ideally adjacent to the kitchen, in order to move food with ease between the two rooms. If the dining area is for entertaining purposes then a location close to the living room opens up a linking of social functions, passing easily from relaxing to eating without loosing the congenial mood.
A dining room has to be accessible throughout the day, with differing emphasis being placed on different meals with breakfast, lunch or the evening meal being the family focus.

The lighting of the room is essential, natural daylight gives a warm welcoming airy feel, ideal for breakfast and lunch. Whereas the subtle use of low lighting creates an intimate feel. Lighting is required to define space and create ambience. Traditionally a low light centrally located would reinforce the table as the focus of the room. Today modern lighting directed at the table offers the same result.

Locating the dining room on the western side of the house allows the evening sunlight to be filtered into the room. Introducing french doors or a patio area creates a link with outside and provides a natural link with the garden for barbecues.

The dining room doubles as a study, a games room, an office and a playroom. In fact it can take on a variety of roles during the evolution of a family unit. With a large family, the extra room becomes essential with the potential of varying activities that will occur throughout the house making it one of the house most useful rooms.

For a small house the use of a combined kitchen dining area offers a more practical solution although it is important to demarcate the cooking and dining areas. A simple change in floor finish, using timber for the dining and tiles in the kitchen will give the desired separation. The use of a split level, practically separating the two spaces will give individual identity to both kitchen and dining. It is important however to treat each area sensitively with lighting and finishes to suit both functions.

When an eating room is part of the kitchen it may require isolation. The provision of waist high kitchen or storage units will define the areas and provide storage and worktop facilities at the same time. Decorative screens can be used to enclose the eating area for special occasions.

The ideal eating room could double as a playroom, study or gallery. It could be a lobby room or a sun trap for plants. The functional aspects should not restrict the imagination. A successful dining room can show flair and imagination.

RANGES

However appealing your might find the idea of a traditional farmhouse kitchen, it is unlikely that you will want to cope with a traditional farmhouse inglenook fire, complete with stockpot, or a black-leaded range. Happily, you can combine traditional looks with efficient performance. Ranges and stoves now mix rustic appeal with modern needs and can be fuelled by gas, electricity, LPG, wood or solid fuel. Running costs are reasonable – especially if you also use it for hot water and central heating.

Most manufacturers provide a dual system, which can provide for both cooking and heating. Your choice very much depends on your requirements, such as regular use for cooking, high demand for domestic hot water, room heating or aesthetics, if you wish to create a focal point within a room.

Heavy insulation means that the range won't make the kitchen too hot in the summer, so it can be left working all year round. Central heating ranges do have a "hot water only" option. Some cooks insist on a second electric single oven, but this isn't necessary.

Make sure to check the power output available from your chosen range if sufficient to adequately supply enough radiators throughout the house. You may be relying on the range for the total central heating or as a back-up. Confirm the power output with your suppliers before purchasing.

Your choice of appliances may also be governed by how it is going to look. Colour choice is very much up to the individual. The stove can be built into a decorative surrounding and this can be used in a practical way as well, with built in niches or shelves, for cooking utensils or ornaments. A stove may also be built into a run of kitchen units.

Very often the decision to choose a range is influenced by a past association with a traditional or farming background. If you are only requiring a feature heat source for the room you may find that a small stove without hotplates or cooking facilities is more appropriate to your needs. They are much less bulky and can match the heating capacity of the traditional range.

The dimensions of your kitchen and the overall size of your house may be the most important consideration governing your choice.

Your architect and local heating engineer will discuss all the options with you and assist in making the final choice.

Ranges are available in up to nine colours depending upon the model chosen, offering a finish compatible with traditional and contemporary surroundings.

Valencia

Designed for a steeply sloping or stepped site. The entrance is to the back and at upper floor level and gives access to the public rooms. The living space will be flooded with natural light all year round thanks to the full height glazing. Sliding doors open onto the balcony.

At lower floor level the W.C. situated between the two bedrooms may, if preferred, be replaced with an access route to the terrace.

(continued over leaf)

DIMENSIONS & AREAS

LIVING	17' 5" x 19' 0"
KITCHEN	9' 6" x 11' 2"
DINING	14' 3" x 10' 2"
LENGTH	42' 8"
FLOOR AREA	1388 sq. ft.

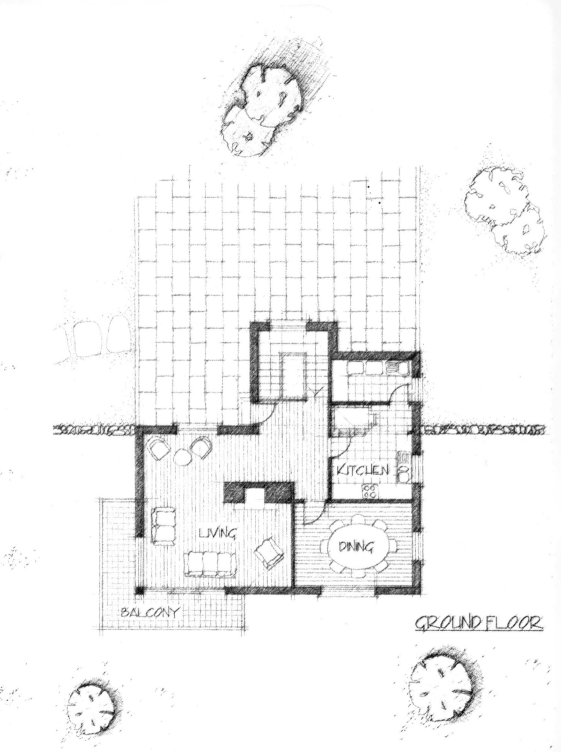

BALCONY

LIVING

KITCHEN

DINING

GROUND FLOOR

Valencia

(continued from previous page)

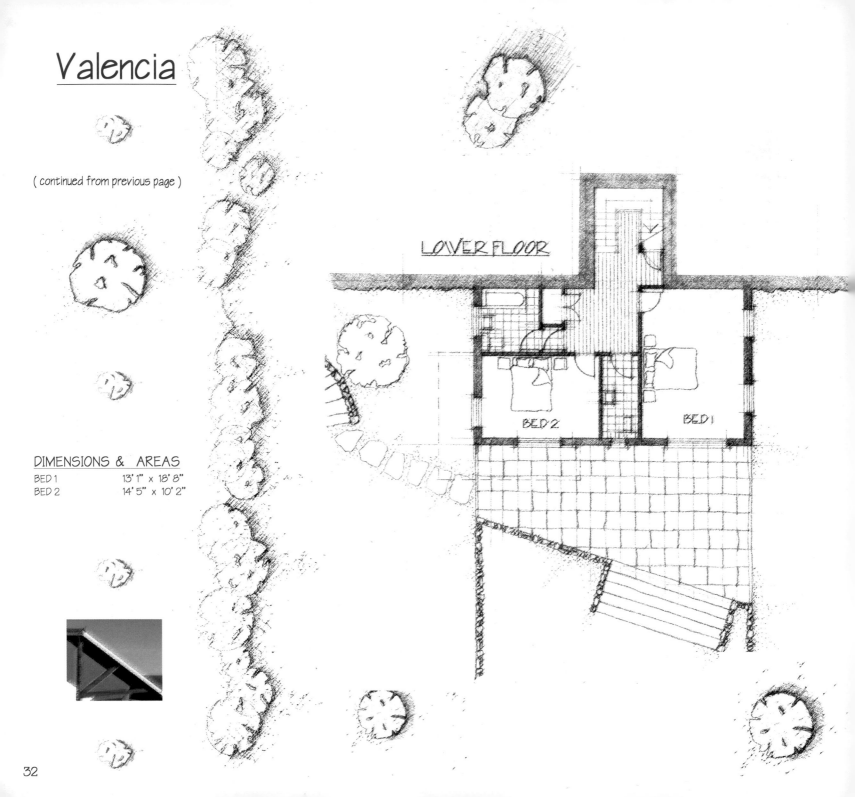

LOVER FLOOR

BED 2

BED 1

DIMENSIONS & AREAS

BED 1	13' 1" x 18' 8"
BED 2	14' 5" x 10' 2"

Little Skellig

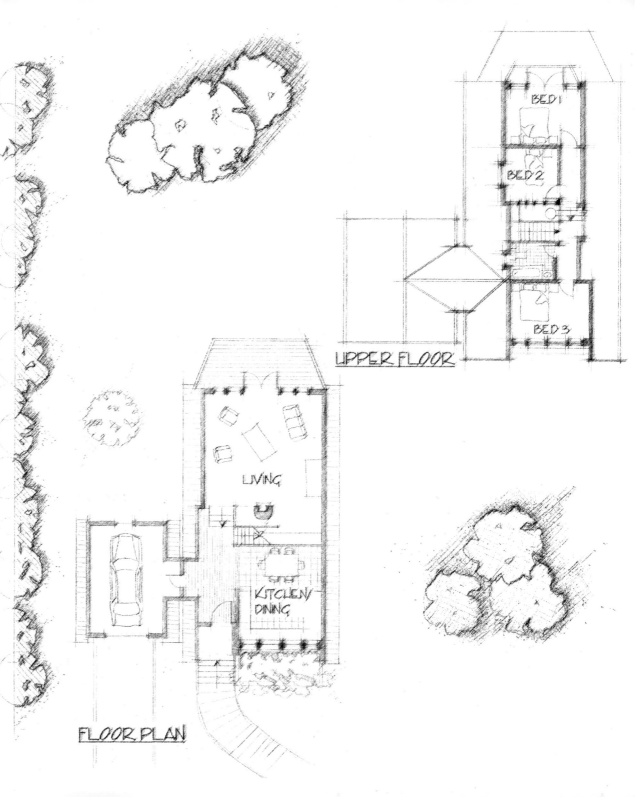

The dramatic roof lines of this two bedroom holiday home would best suit a hilly, well forested location. Designs similar to this can be found in the north of Scotland and parts of Scandinavia.
The large areas of glazing at each end of the house permit a flood of natural light throughout the ground floor.

DIMENSIONS & AREAS

LIVING	21' 0" x 26' 7"
KITCHEN	14' 9" x 17' 1"
BED 1	13' 9" x 9' 10"
BED 2	9' 8" x 8' 10"
BED 3	13' 9" x 11' 2"
LENGTH	42' 0"
FLOOR AREA	998 sq. ft.

UPPER FLOOR

FLOOR PLAN

Mucklabeg

The square plan form of this design dictates the hipped roof which is then crowned by a little decorative ironwork. Whilst the coloured render and bands may not be appropriate to your site or taste the intention of the illustration is to show the potential that colour can offer.

The internal lobby contains a small window giving a glimpse of the living room.

DIMENSIONS & AREAS

LIVING	14' 1" x 15' 5"
KITCHEN	14' 1" x 15' 1"
BED 1	12' 2" x 11' 5"
BED 2	12' 2" x 11' 5"
LENGTH	32' 10"
FLOOR AREA	932 sq. ft.

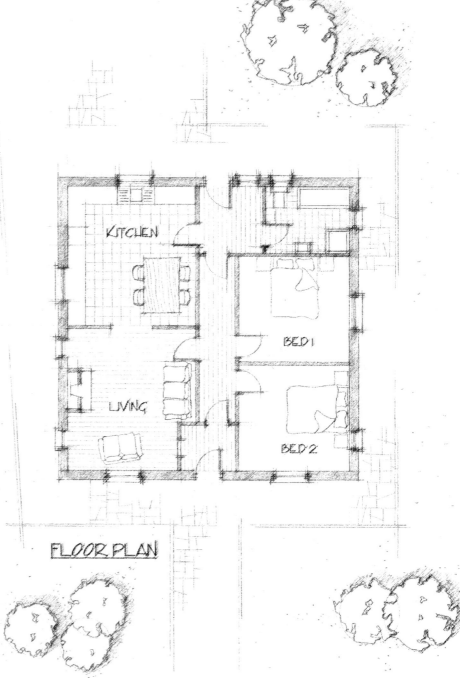

FLOOR PLAN

Inish Ge

The main living spaces on the ground floor are arranged to the front and sides in open plan, with ancillary accomodation situated to the rear and accessed from a small hallway.

The spatial quality of this open plan design is further enhanced by areas of double height either side of the feature spiral staircase.

The area to the left of the stair has been included within the dimensions of the living room but does infact create a wee snug or study room.

DIMENSIONS & AREAS

LIVING	30' 10" x 15' 9"
KITCHEN	8' 10" x 13' 0"
BED 1	12' 2" x 11' 5"
BED 2	12' 2" x 11' 5"
LENGTH	32' 10"
FLOOR AREA	932 sq. ft.

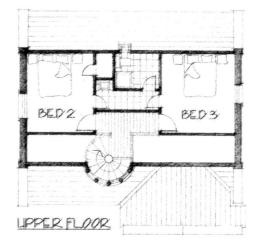

UPPER FLOOR

BED 2   BED 3

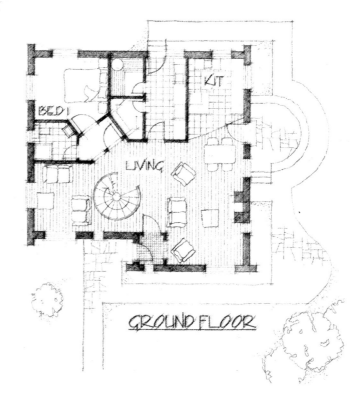

BED 1   KIT   LIVING

GROUND FLOOR

39

Inishdooey

L ocating the main living area at first floor, coupled with large areas of glazing, give this modest scaled dwelling a light open feeling, with the living room glazing capable of exploiting any views.

This traditional vernacular dwelling offers a contemporary alternative behind the facade.

DIMENSIONS & AREAS

LIVING	15' 9" x 24' 7"
KITCHEN	14' 1" x 24' 7"
BED 1	15' 9" x 11' 10"
BED 2	9' 2" x 12' 6"
BED 3	14' 1" x 13' 3"
LENGTH	39' 4"
FLOOR AREA	1755 sq. ft.

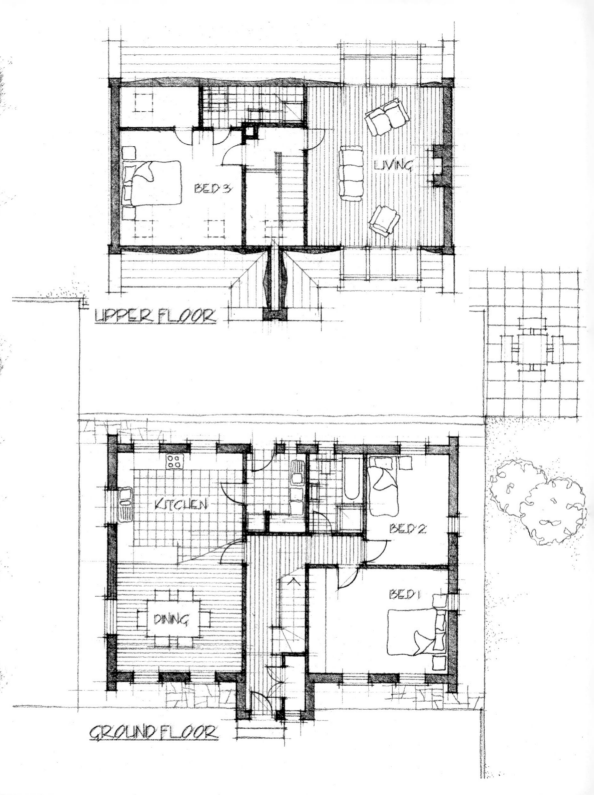

UPPER FLOOR

BED 3

LIVING

GROUND FLOOR

KITCHEN

DINING

BED 2

BED 1

Carrig

This three bedroom dormer bungalow suits a slightly sloping south facing site with large glazed areas serving all the living spaces. The lounge has a vaulted ceiling overlooked by the first floor landing. Upon entering the house one is greeted with a large vaulted entrance with top light through the roof, a feature bridge landing to the master bedroom offers extra interest.

DIMENSIONS & AREAS

LIVING	10' 6" x 13' 2"
KITCHEN	10' 6" x 10' 7"
LOUNGE	12' 10" x 12' 2"
SUN LOUNGE	12' 5" x 7' 7"
BED 1	9' 11" x 11' 6"
BED 2	13' 1" x 11' 6"
BED 3	10' 6" x 11' 6"
LENGTH	44' 3"
FLOOR AREA	1360 sq. ft.

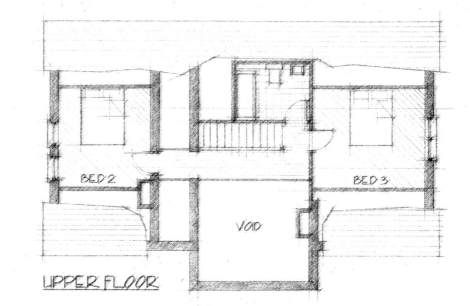

UPPER FLOOR

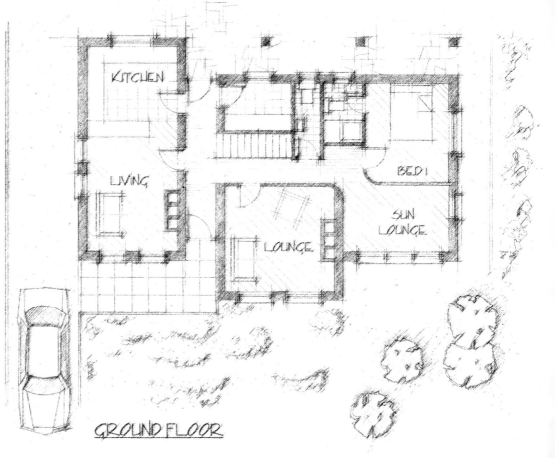

GROUND FLOOR

43

Tory

The pleasing simplicity of the facade is created by its symmetry. Internally, however, the main living spaces differ in size with the wide, off centre, hallway being the cause. The two bedrooms within the roof are particularly spacious and there is ample storage space throughout the house -a consideration often neglected in more modern designs.

DIMENSIONS & AREAS

LIVING	14' 9" x 14' 6"
KITCHEN	10' 10" x 10' 9"
LOUNGE	12' 8" x 14' 7"
BED 1	10' 0" x 10' 3"
BED 2	12' 8" x 17' 0"
BED 3	13' 5" x 17' 0"
LENGTH	37' 9"
FLOOR AREA	1687 sq. ft.

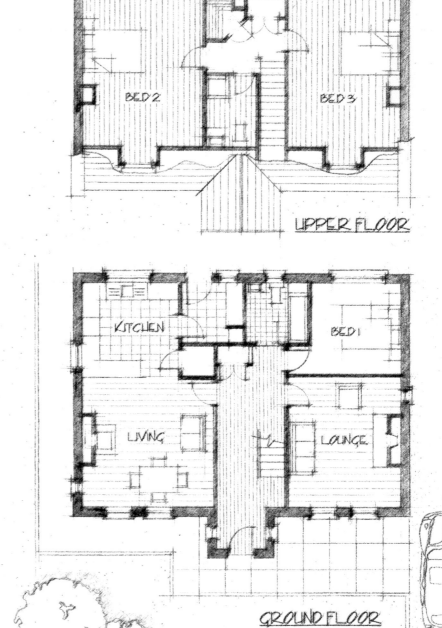

UPPER FLOOR

GROUND FLOOR

44

45

Tegral Building Products Ltd.

The Tegral Group is the leading Irish manufacturer of roofing and cladding products for the commercial, industrial, domestic and agricultural markets in Ireland. From it's strategically located operations Tegral Building Products supplies a diverse range of quality products from Fibre Cement slates, Natural Slates, Clay Tiles and Corrugated sheets to Ridge Tiles, Thrutex High Performing Roofing Felt, Tyvek Breather Membrane, Harcon Ventilation Products, Pressed Slate Trim and various other roofing accessories.

Customers of Tegral Building Products Ltd. are assured the most technologically advanced product within a fixed time frame and to a quality standard which is consistent to with their individual requirements. Marketing and Sales is through our sales team and builders providers situated in a number of locations around the country. An unrivalled position has been established in Ireland by the company based on over sixty years experience in the building construction industry.

Thrutone 2000

The new Thrutone 2000 slates with a tempting range of shapes, colours, sizes and a choice of surface finish allow the designer or houseowner the freedom to design. In addition this range is manafactured under the ISO 9002 Quality Management System. In Ireland a tradition has been established for pitched, slated roofs. It has been found that this style of roofing is not only visually pleasing but affords the best protection from our severe weather conditions. A well pitched slated roof is secure against high winds, impenetrable to heavy rain and stands the test of time. The Thrutone 2000 range provides the most attractive solution for the severe weather conditions encoun-tered in this part of Europe. The Thrutone 2000 range allows the designer or houseowner freedom to design with size, shape, colour and surface.

Thrutone 2000 slates are available in a range of sizes. The availability of slates in smaller sizes provides greater flexibility in roof design. They are also suitable for use on much admired curved roofs. Advice is readily available to ensure correct application.

The traditional rectangular shape provides a very satisifying appearance. In addition chamfered, scalloped and bullnosed shaped Thrutone slates maybe used to introduce areas of visual interest in rectangular slating by offering banding and feature possibilities.

When it comes to colour once again Thrutone 2000 can offer a multiple choice. The colours available are Slate-Grey, Blue-Black, Turf-Brown, Stone-Green, Heather and Terracotta. These colours reflecting the

environment allow the designer or houseowner to enhance a building with a roof finished to complement the other materials used.

Thrutone 2000 slates are available with either a smooth finish or a textured surface in each colour. The surface finish options allow for subtle variations be chosen in the overall appearance of the slated roof or wall area. The textured surface of Thrutone 2000 relief captures the appearance of traditional slate and gives an additional visual depth.

Classic Natural Slate

Natural slate is unique. Formed deep in the earth as long ago as 450 million years by the same colossal internal pressures which created mountain ranges, it will endure every extreme of the elements.

Classic Natural Slate is a superbly practical roofing material, will last for generations and when expertly laid costs virtually nothing to maintain.

From various Quarries throughout the world come slate of inherently differing colours and textures. All of the very finest quality, but each suiting an aspect of architecture complement-ing a hue of brick or stone - each blending with a particular style of structure.

We have years of experience in sourcing the world's finest slates, from the famous regions of Wales, England, Spain and North and South Amercia, and can advise on the right slate for your own individual building project.

Our expertise in one of the world's finest natural building resources provides the customer with roofing of exceptional durability, practicality - and classic, ageless, beauty.

Clay Plain Tiles

Our Acme range of of Plain Clay Tiles include both machine made and hand made clay tiles.

The unique range of machine made clay plain tiles, complemented by their range of fittings, provides an opportunity for designers and houseowners to achieve first class roofs which combine the benefits of advance manufacturing techniques with the charm and warmth associated with traditional roofscapes. There is an extensive range of colours and products available. The small unit size of these tiles combines with the wide range of fittings available to make an ideal choice for creative roof design.

The colour and character of Acme tiles provide a lasting beauty, warmth and most importantly they improve in appearance with every passing season.

The skills of the craftsmen who create the Acme range of handmade Clay Tiles and fittings have been handed down through generations. It is this human touch which help to give Acme handmades their inimitable warmth, character and mellow beauty, whilst their granular texture and slight random irregularities make each individual tile unique.

Other roofing material which Tegral Building Products supply include Thrutex High Performance Felt which unlike some traditional type IF roofing felts which are prone to brittleness and disintegration over time, Thrutex felts are rot proof and can confidently be expected to last the lifetime of a roof structure. Tyvek Beather Membrane is a remarkable material which is waterproof and windtight yet has extremely high vapour permeability. These properties make it ideally suited for use as an underlay in slated or sheeted roofs. Harcon Ventilation Systems provides a wide range of ventilation products for your roof, all of which can be used to meet the requirements of the building regulations Part F 1997. Pressed Slate trims adds to the appearance of the roof while also permanently securing slates on gables and valleys thus preventing storm damage. Tools and Fittings are also available for your roof.

We have a Sales Team and a Technical Services Department who are available to assist you with your individual roofing requirements.

Inishbiggle

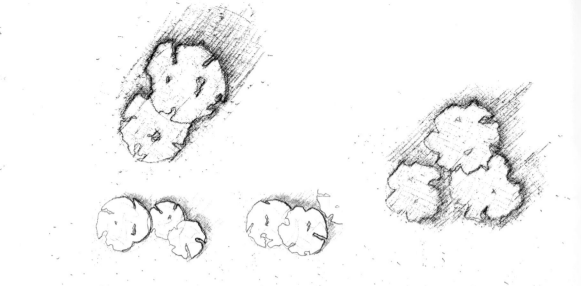

The charm of the old; here is a bold block situated on a sloping linear site.

Illustrated here with three bedrooms this could easily be altered to two with bedroom 1 and the living room becoming one large public space with a central hearth as feature. This is a good example of plan versatility.

DIMENSIONS & AREAS

LIVING	13' 9" x 17' 9"
KITCHEN	15' 1" x 17' 9"
BED 1	12' 10" x 11' 6"
BED 2	11' 2" x 13' 1"
BED 3	11' 10" x 11' 4"
LENGTH	70' 6"
FLOOR AREA	1215 sq. ft.

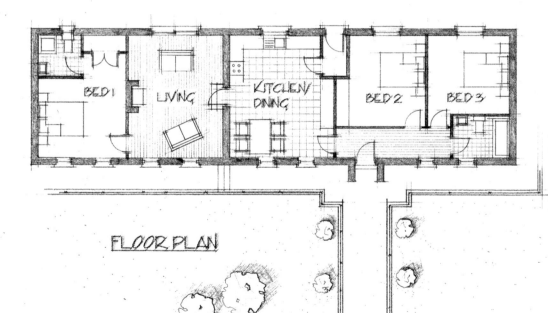

FLOOR PLAN

Sherkin

Continuing the linear approach, this design is based on the traditional workers cottages. Illustrated here as terraced housing this design may suit a developer wishing to build a number of holiday units.
Alternatively, it could become one long single cottage giving double the areas shown below.
As with most designs in this book the material finishes shown may not prove appropriate to site and may require alteration.

DIMENSIONS & AREAS

LIVING/KITCHEN	9' 10" x 21' 8"
LOUNGE	9' 10" x 21' 8"
BED 1	11' 8" x 14' 5"
LENGTH	36' 7"
FLOOR AREA	780 sq. ft.

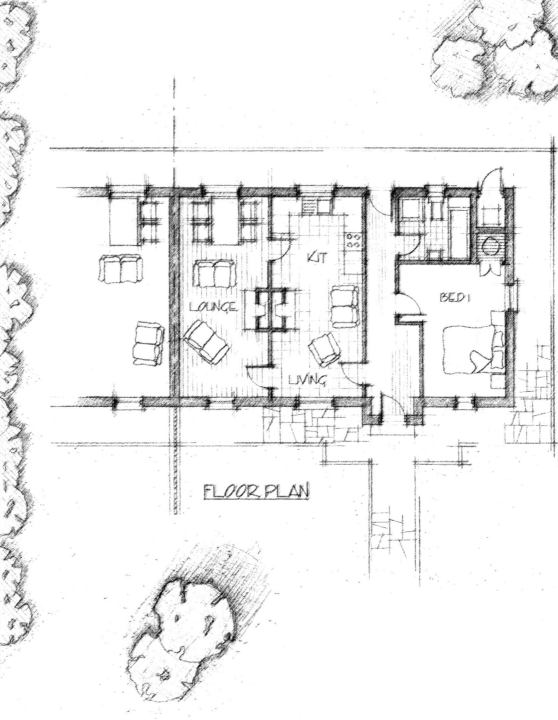

FLOOR PLAN

Saint MacDara

The excitement of this three bedroom dormer is generated by the architects use of materials - a selected area of natural stone, exposed timber rafters, creating a terraced frontage, and the natural slate roof.

Internally each bedroom has the luxury of an en-suite, an increasingly popular requirement of the holiday home.

The lounge is double height and fills with natural light via large areas of glazing and the middle dormer window.

DIMENSIONS & AREAS

LIVING	.10' 2" x 11' 6"
KITCHEN	9' 10" x 9' 10"
LOUNGE	14' 9" x 11' 6"
BED 1	11' 6" x 9' 10"
BED 2	11' 6" x 9' 10"
BED 3	14' 9" x 13' 2"
LENGTH	43' 5"
FLOOR AREA	1419 sq. ft.

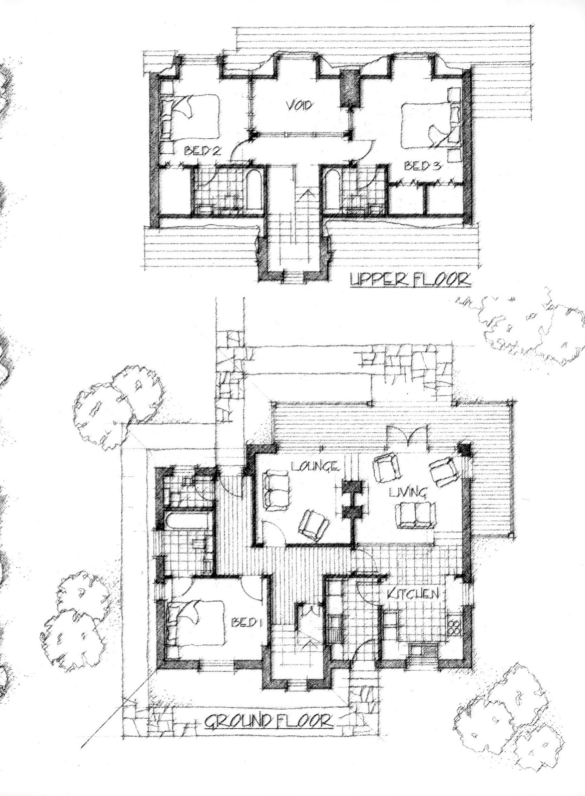

UPPER FLOOR

GROUND FLOOR

Coney

Aluxurious two bedroom house designed for a sloping site and a north - south axis. The lounge must have a southerly aspect, then, because of its generous glazing, it will benefit from full natural light throughout the day.

The master bedroom opens onto a private terrace which is made private by the extended parapet wall.

(continued over leaf).

DIMENSIONS & AREAS

LIVING	17' 5" x 10' 10"
KITCHEN/DINING	11' 2" x 20' 4"
LOUNGE	16' 5" x 14' 5"
LENGTH	35' 5"
FLOOR AREA	1602 sq. ft.

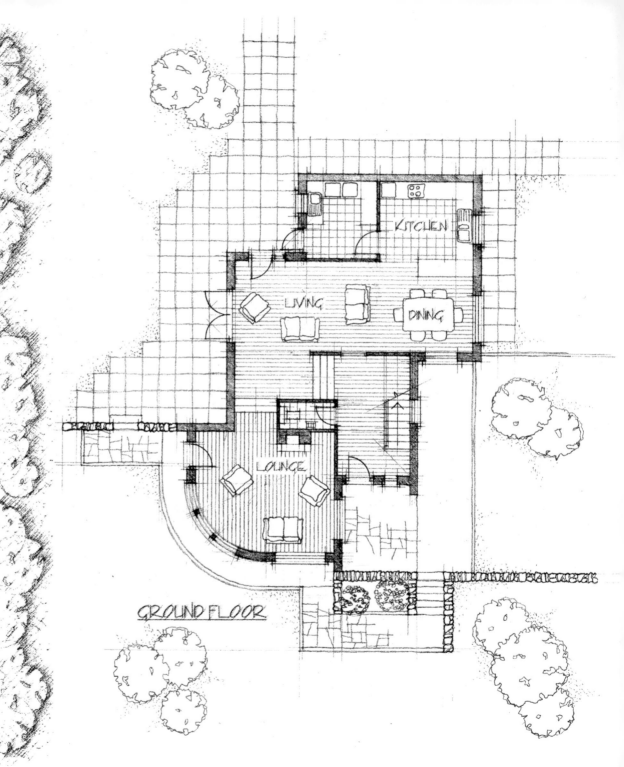

KITCHEN

LIVING

DINING

LOUNGE

GROUND FLOOR

Coney

Continued from previous page

DIMENSIONS & AREAS

BED 1   11' 6" x 13' 1"
BED 2   11' 6" x 20' 0"

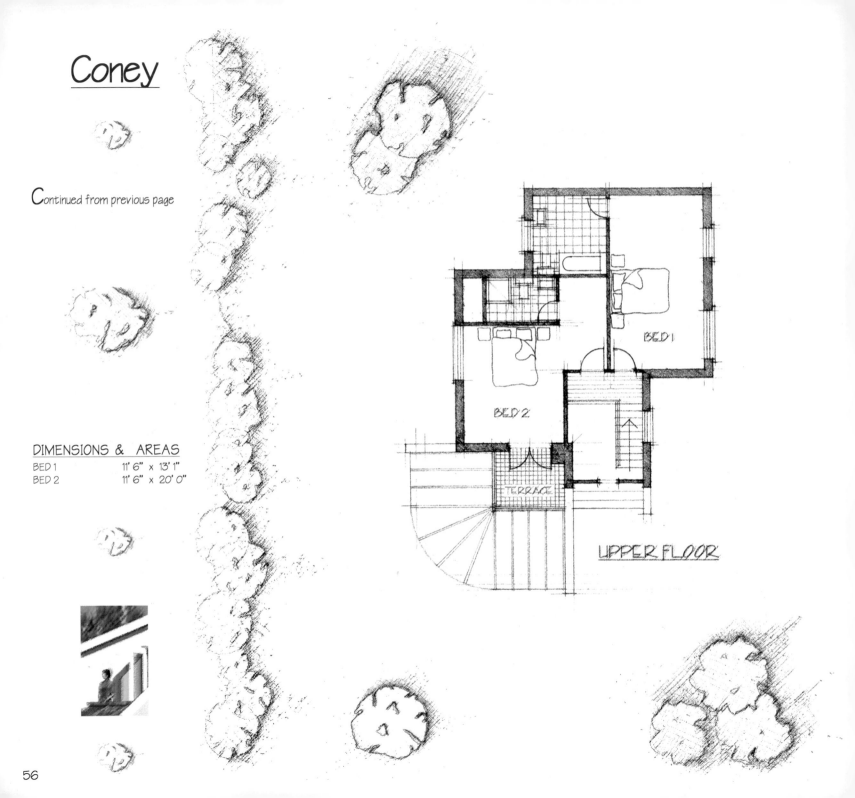

BED 1

BED 2

TERRACE

UPPER FLOOR

Inishglora

The marriage of traditional and contemporary themes give this dormer bungalow a subtle blend of space and finishes. The centre of the house is top lit from rooflights filtering light down past the landing balcony to the ground floor hallway. The number of bedrooms can be increased to five by utilising the roof space. (Continued over page).

DIMENSIONS & AREAS

LIVING	13' 2" x 15' 3"
KITCHEN	11' 10" x 13' 2"
LOUNGE	15' 9" x 15' 3"
DINING	13' 6" x 15' 3"
BED 1	13' 2" x 15' 3"
BED 2	14' 1" x 19' 0"
LENGTH	60' 4"
FLOOR AREA	3350 sq. ft.

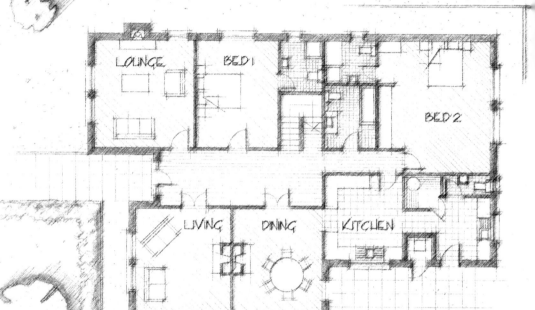

LOUNGE BED 1 BED 2

LIVING DINING KITCHEN

GROUND FLOOR

Inishglora

(Continued from previous page).

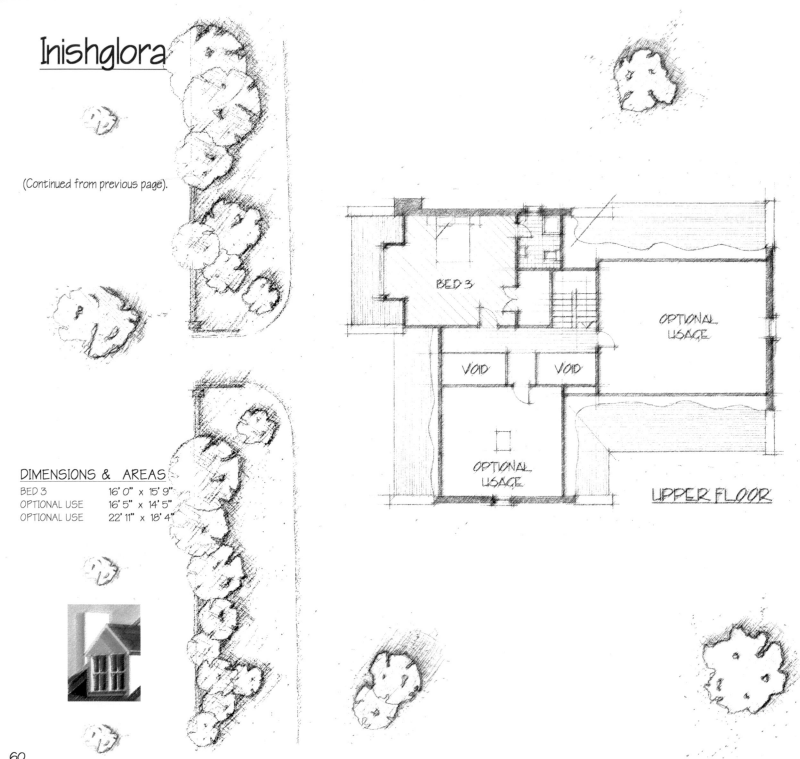

DIMENSIONS & AREAS

BED 3	16' 0" x 15' 9"
OPTIONAL USE	16' 5" x 14' 5"
OPTIONAL USE	22' 11" x 18' 4"

BED 3

OPTIONAL USAGE

VOID

VOID

OPTIONAL USAGE

UPPER FLOOR

Achill

Based on a vernacular theme, this house is very much open plan with the living room, kitchen and dining areas all utilising the same space with a traditional bed outcrop located adjacent to the open fire in the living room.

The vaulted ceiling feature over the living area is continued over the first floor bedroom which has a full height glazed opening reflecting the traditional barn door accessed from an external stair.

DIMENSIONS & AREAS

LIVING/KITCHEN	24' 7" x 16' 5"
BED 1	11' 2" x 19' 8"
BED 2	11' 2" x 16' 5"
LENGTH	44' 11"
FLOOR AREA	1037 sq. ft.

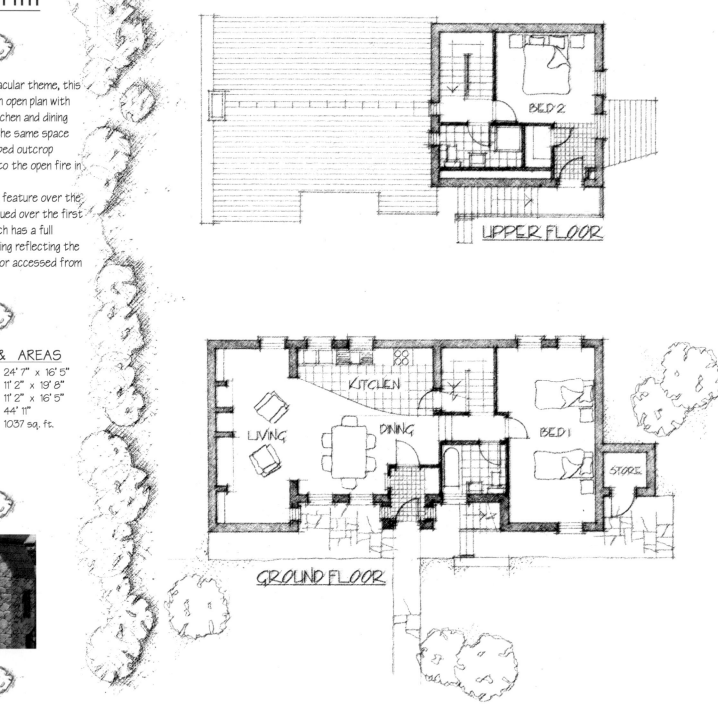

UPPER FLOOR

GROUND FLOOR

Chapel

The entrance hall opens onto a double height living area which is given additional natural top light through velux windows.

Upper floor bedrooms and landing also benefit greatly from the roof light that runs the length of the building.

The private terrace would be a place of quiet reflection amidst the creeping ivy.

DIMENSIONS & AREAS

LIVING	24' 1" x 11' 8"
KITCHEN	14' 9" x 11' 8"
DINING	14' 9" x 11' 8"
BED 1	11' 2" x 11' 8"
BED 2	14' 9" x 11' 8"
BED 2	17' 5" x 11' 8"
LENGTH	52' 2"
FLOOR AREA	1711 sq. ft.

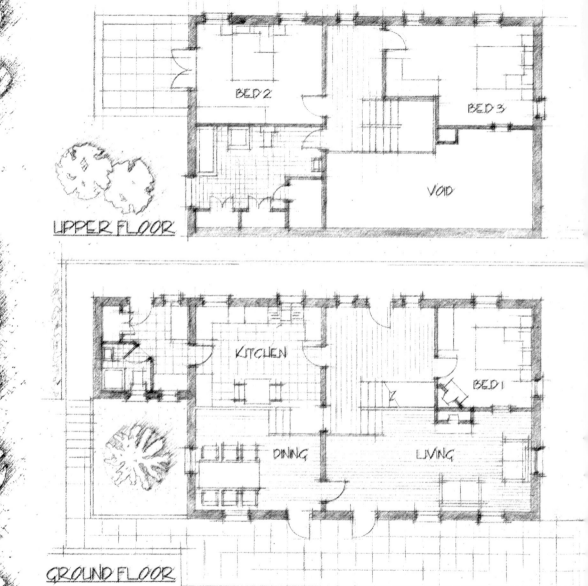

UPPER FLOOR

BED 2

BED 3

VOID

GROUND FLOOR

KITCHEN

BED 1

DINING

LIVING

LIVING ROOMS AND LOUNGES

These rooms are variously referred to as parlours, drawing rooms, dens, sitting rooms, and so on. The variety of names reflects the range of design approaches possible, but all refer to areas that are, essentially, gathering spaces in the home.

A comfortable living-room where you can sit back and relax, letting the worries of the day ebb away, is an essential part of any home and can play a major role in the social life within the dwelling. On the other hand, it can be that room within a home which may simply be a private refuge or den away from the hustle often associated with the kitchen/general living areas. It can also take the shape of a more formal lounge along the lines of the old parlour or "good room" - seldom used except on those rare occasions when visitors called and, of course, at Christmas. The parlour was a room which always created an impression on the people who frequented it, from the child who was rarely allowed within its hallowed walls to the adult who remembers the atmosphere and essence of the parlour of his youth with a nostalgia, and with a longing to recreate that place within his new home.

Whether there are one, two or even three of these rooms within a dwelling will largely depend on your own individual require-ments and lifestyle, and on the needs of family and children. Your own intuition is vital in getting the design right. While on a practical level a design can be tested for its workability, there is no such easy solution to knowing if it will come to life for you. Many people feel that their ideas and feelings stem from an emotional or whimsical basis and that they cannot be practically justified, and so can often dismiss them as too personal to be relevant to discussions regarding their new home.

The client's intuition can provide the architect with guidelines, particularly in answer to the all-important question: *What makes you feel comfortable?* It may be light, open spaces, a view, internal features or maybe well-defined rooms. Hence, it is good to throw out all your ideas for discussion. Then they can be looked at from all points of view such as design, workability and, of course, the ever-important but often forgotten budget.

The living-room , as with all rooms and their relationships are constantly changing both in size and role - shedding old ones and adopting new. While privacy is important and separate rooms such as bedrooms and bathrooms are still needed, the opening up of the living areas can be considered and has become increasingly popular with a move away from the clearly defined specific-use rooms like the parlour of former times. This is often achieved by combining rooms such as lounge/living/kitchen/dining into an all-encompassing open plan living area as is popular in many European countries. The space can be portioned out so that several people can happily share these areas while engaged in different activities. Nooks and crannies can be created with the overall space if so desired. Often the boundaries of the individual spaces can be delineated by the specific placement of furniture, change in level, variation of floor covering or possibly the introduction of vertical columns, bookshelves etc. Alternatively and possibly the most common today in Ireland - particularly since the kitchen has regained its position as the focus of the home - is the kitchen/dining/living room with the more formal lounge accessed off this area - possibly through a glazed screen or doors. This allows the rooms to be used individually where one can enjoy the luxury of a leisurely Sunday morning cup of coffee with a stack of papers or a good book while life goes on roundabout. Alternatively, both rooms may be opened up for a function or gathering of people where an evening can progress from cooking to eating and on to relaxing in the lounge area.

In planning a lounge or living room one needs to be careful when deciding on the overall size and scale. Often, if moving from an existing dwelling where the room in question was too small, there can be a tendency to overcompensate in the proposed dwelling. The room should be large enough to carry out its function but not so large (and this applies particularly to a family room) that it loses its character and cosiness.

Where a large formal lounge is required it is often possible to incorporate a dining area within the room. This can be located on a different level or possibly within a projection bay. The need for a formal and separate dining room can then be eliminated giving maximum space to the lounge when needed.

The location of the living room and lounge (if separate rooms) would normally be such that their is a natural progression of sunlight from easterly morning sun in the kitchen through to the general living area during the day with the setting sun in the living area/lounge i.e. evening room. Having said this, however, where one's lifestyle is such that little if any time is spent in the kitchen area in the morning this may be altered to include sunlight to the kitchen/living area in the evening. This is a very personal and important decision and one where the intuition mentioned earlier has to be utilized.

The views, if one is lucky enough to have them, are also very important. It is generally felt that the view should be given to those rooms which get most use during the daytime hours such as kitchens and living rooms. Beware, however, not to sacrifice the light in favour of view. Though this is not a priority for everybody, most people will find that while a view is uplifting and there to be appreciated, it is generally a background feature of which one is only sporadically aware, while the presence of sunlight in the rooms in which most of the day is spent is of vital importance.

When all is said and done often it will be those last touches which will bring the rooms to life and instill character in them. This may be the paint colour, floor covering or perhaps a piece of personal furniture or a beautiful fireplace adorning the focal point of the room - possibly the last bastion of nostalgia in these centrally heated times.

LIGHTING

Background lighting which is used to produce light in the absence of natural lighting offers an opportunity to develop a light strategy within a house and produce dynamic results. The single most effective method of changing the character or feel of a space is the careful placing/arrangement of lighting. In most houses artificial lighting is provided by ceiling- mounted pendant fittings or wall mounted lamps. Another popular form of lighting used in the more utilitarian areas of the home is fluorescent tubes which produce a quality of light more commonly used within the work office environment. The light produced by such lamps is bright and high in contrast which can lead to shadows and glare.

Within the house, artificial lighting can be used to fulfill a number of different functions ranging from task to atmospheric lighting. Generally, task lighting is created by concentrating the light from a number of sources to illuminate one bright surface for reading or viewing. It is generally more suitable to use the light from a number of different lamps in a bid to eliminate shadows.
Atmospheric lighting is used to create mood lighting. Unlike task lighting, mood lighting is concerned with the deliberate creation of shadows and tones with light sources placed at low light levels and up-lighters and other lamp arrangements gainfully employed to create theatrical effects. Subtle lights may be used to reflect on a range of surfaces.

Planning

Before one develops and finalises a lighting plan it is worth spending some time familiarising oneself with the latest technology in light and lamp fitting. Lamp design has developed tremendously in the last ten years. Lamps are designed to create an array of different effects such as imitating natural light or creating patterns on surfaces.

Plan your lighting layout in such a way as to allow flexibility for further development. Changing the furniture layout within a room could dramatically alter the light requirements and this point should be borne in mind when scheduling light and electrical layout.

Lighting design must take account of safety and comfort of the users as its primary consideration. Light levels, direction and quality must therefore, be designed to suit the physical limitations of the user - for example, the very young and the elderly may require enhanced light levels on stairs.

Cables leading to lamps should be located in areas bearing in mind the hazards they may create. A broken lamp filament or cord can present a potentially lethal risk.

Special attention needs to be paid to ensure areas of particular risk are illuminated to an acceptable standard. Such areas include treads of steps, kitchen surfaces and bathrooms.

Light Requirements in Traditional Areas

Living Rooms
Commonly, diffused lights, down-, up- or pendant lights provide background light. Accent lighting in other areas of the room could be used to focus on a specific object. Adaptability is the key for lighting arrangements in this room. It is also important to bear in mind the different uses to which the room may be put and allow a lighting pattern which allows for these.

Studies
More and more commonly, the equipment to be found within the study is electrically powered - computers, keyboard, typewriters etc - and the selection of lamp fitting for this room will require careful consideration in order to omit glare and provide a light low in contrast to or of equal intensity with the screens or monitors.

Bedrooms
Within most bedrooms there are three types of activity which require different types of lighting: general light, reading and dressing. Centrally mounted lamps, ceiling pendants may be used to provide general lighting with bedside lamps for reading and recessed spotlight may be used for providing crisp floodlights for dressing.

Bathrooms
Safety is the main consideration for the layout of lighting in this room. No lamp fitting should be exposed within this room and light switches are required to be located outside the bathrooms unless switches are operated by a pull cord.
Commonly, recessed mounted down-lighters and, more recently, low voltage lamps allow fittings to be positioned where previously it would have been considered dangerous. Reflector fittings offer a good method of providing high quality general background lighting.

Methods of Lighting

Tungsten Uplights: These could be also of the tungsten halogen lamp type dependent on the quality of light preferred.

Tungsten Halogen Stand Up-Lighters: Provide clean white light which highlights details of walls and ceilings. Minor defects in walls and ceilings may be exaggerated by the above method and care should be taken to ensure that this is the most appropriate form of lighting.

Standard Tungsten Pendant: The traditional method of background lighting to rooms.

Recess Tungsten Down-Lighting: Creates a spot/shaft of light with the light source hidden at oblique angles.

Tungsten Parabolic Spotlight: Creates a warm glowing background light.

Standard Spotlight: On floor stand with direction variable lamp offers an adaptable alternative.

Table Lamp: Traditional form of lighting to local areas of the room.

Hardwood Floors

In decorating a room, the creation of an atmosphere and feel, which is both cosy and comfortable, and which is durable and puts up with constant use, are critical factors. It is vital that the basic materials used, are easy to harmonise with any furniture and fabrics used. As styles and fashion evolve over the years, so will room furnishings and fabrics, and it is important that in giving a room a little 'tweak', will not result in the necessity of a total make over.

The choice of floor covering is therefore critical. It must be durable, economic, aesthetically pleasing, and have the ability to be in harmony with, and match, the furniture and fabrics used in the room. It must also be hygienic, and easily cleaned and maintained.

Hardwood floors are a natural choice, as they satisfy all of the demands outlined above. The popularity of hardwood floors has escalated quite dramatically in recent years, to the point that they have become 'de rigeur' .

Wood is classified into two types, softwood and hardwood. Softwood comes in the main from evergreen or non-deciduous trees, which grow relatively quickly, while hardwood comes in the main from deciduous trees, that is, trees that shed their leaves in winter. Deciduous trees, in temperate climates tend to grow very slowly. That slowness in growth makes for a very close and tight grain structure, and results in a wood that is extremely dense, hard and durable, hence the name - hardwood.

There are many species of hardwood grown throughout the world, and as a traded commodity internationally, wood is second only to oil and oil derivatives. Wood is unique, in that it is probably the most environmentally friendly modern building material. It differs from most other modern building materials, in that it can be renewed, and regenerated. Most other building materials used in the construction of a modern home come "out of a hole in the ground", and are not naturally regenerated or renewed. For flooring, the popular species of hardwood normally used are Oak, Hard Maple (also known as Sugar Maple), Beech, Ash, Iroko Teak, and Merbau Mahogany.

This range of species is popular because they give a choice of colours and grain patterns which will match in with most, if not all decor requirements.

The escalation in the popularity of hardwood floors in the modern home, coincides with relatively recent technological innovations, which allow for the hardwood floors to be 'pre-finished', that is, that the boards are precision machined and lacquered in the factory, prior to being delivered on-site for fitting. Another recent innovation, is in the machining of the boards, which allow the boards to be fitted without the requirement of nailing or fixing them to the sub-floor, what is commonly known as a 'floating' floor.

Hygiene is always a factor in the choice of floor covering, and invariably in the past this meant that those choices were restricted and style and quality sacrificed, or that the level of hygiene was compromised. With hardwood floors, these sacrifices and compromises are not required. Hardwood floors are the epitome of style and fashion, they are easy to maintain and keep clean. There is no environment for the dust mite to hide and live. A hardwood floor can be swept clean in a matter of minutes, and the vacuum cleaner will make short work of it. They diminish drudgery, as washing hardwood floors is not allowed, all that is needed is a wipe with a dampened cloth. Scuff marks rub off with ease, and in the case of a very difficult mark, a soft cloth damped with white spirit will usually do the trick. If there are children and pets in the home, then it is essential that you know that when you clean the floor, that it is clean, and that there is nothing hidden beneath the fibres.

Common questions about hardwood floors.

At what stage in the building process are the hardwood floors installed or fitted ?
Because a hardwood floor is essentially a decor item, a floor covering material, it is not fitted until after all the other construction work on the house is finished. There are two reasons for this one is that you do not want the floor to be exposed to any damage from construction operations, and the other is, that in a new house, the fabric of the house, especially the sub-floor has to be very well dried out.

70

I am getting a hardwood floor fitted, what should I look out for to satisfy myself that the work is done properly ?

The following is a check list excerpt from the BS standard you might use when inspecting the finished floor:

1. Loose boards or strips,
2. Gaps at joints,
3. Bad fitting, say at hearths or doorways,
4. Nails or screws projecting above the surface,
5. Defective filling of nail holes, if any,
6. Strips or boards out of level with the plane of the floor,
7. Inadequate provision for expansion,
8. Chips or splinters.

Why is there always allowance made for expansion ?

All wood used in construction and furniture must be properly seasoned. Seasoning means that the wood is dried out properly. Hardwoods used for wood floors are dried to a moisture content of about 10%. When a hardwood floor is first fitted in a house, this moisture content in the hardwood floor will tend to rise a little as the floor reaches equilibrium with it's new environment. This slight increase in moisture content will make each board very slightly wider. This consequent increase in width ensures that the boards are pushed very tightly together and there are no unsightly gaps. However the area of a room is finite, and to allow for the increase in width of the boards, provision is always made to allow for this expansion.

The Irish Oak range of Hardwood Floors.

Irish Oak are a company established in Glenties, County Donegal, over ten years ago for the purpose of manufacturing hardwood floors. Over the years, they have manufactured hardwood floors which have been used in very prestigious projects in Ireland and abroad. These include the Government Offices (Department of An Taoiseach), the Beckett Theatre in Trinity College, Céide Fields visitors centre in Mayo, the International Financial Services Centre in Dublin. They have also supplied the hardwood floors for many homes, offices and hotels throughout Ireland. They are, as far as we know, the only manufacturers of 'pre-finished' hardwood floors in Ireland or Britain.

Irish Oak carry an extensive range of hardwood floor products which will suit most budgets and decor requirements. They manufacture two types of board, one is called the 1 Strip which is reminiscent of a plank type floor, and the other is called the 2 Strip, where each board is composed two strips wide, resulting in the finished floor having the modern narrow strip effect. Their manufactured boards are solid hardwood throughout. Their range of hardwood species include Red Oak, White Oak, Maple, Iroko Teak and Merbau Mahogany. Unlike competing brands who base their grades on wood quality, Irish Oak are unique in that they offer only one grade, 'A'. They do however offer three colour grades in their Maple Floors; 'Prime', which is selected for all light colour, 'Country', which is selected for all the natural range of colours in the wood, and 'Mill Run', which is midway between both. They offer a range of choices in fitting all of their manufactured floors. They can be fitted using the traditional secret nailing method, or 'floating', the decision on which method to use is usually left to the fitter. The boards are factory lacquered using Acrylic applied using modern technology, the lacquer is cured or dried in an Ultra Violet tunnel, and all their boards are also sealed on the reverse for added protection and balance.

Inishtrahull

A healthy rural design that opens up internally with a minimal amount of hallway.

The feature spiral stair within the living room helps to conserve floor area and makes for a romantic link to the master bedroom above.

The small sun lounge with its glazed roof could be screened off during the long evenings to create a cosy night around the hearth.

(Continued over page).

DIMENSIONS & AREAS

LIVING	16' 5" x 24' 1"
KITCHEN/DINING	21' 8" x 12' 10"
RECEPTION	9' 10" x 9' 10"
BED 1	11' 6" x 9' 10"
MASTER BED	16' 5" x 18' 0"
LENGTH	48' 11"
FLOOR AREA	1275 sq. ft.

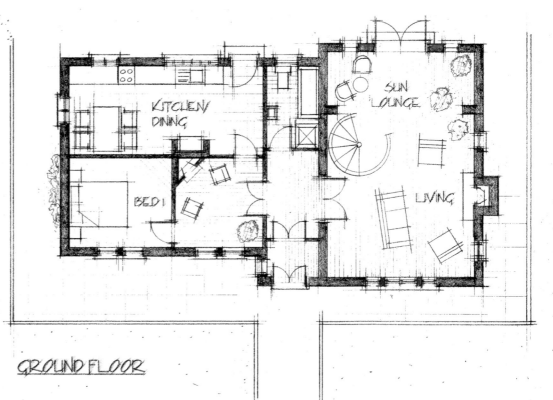

UPPER FLOOR

BED 2

GROUND FLOOR

KITCHEN/DINING

SUN LOUNGE

BED 1

LIVING

Inishturk

The central feature of this spacious three bedroom bungalow is its large, internal sun lounge. With fully glazed double doors to each of its four walls the occupier can open up the living spaces into each other. It also provides an area for children to play on those unfortunate rainy days.

The overspill of natural light and the inevitable solar gain will benefit the entire house.

DIMENSIONS & AREAS

LIVING	16' 1" x 19' 0"
KITCHEN	12' 5" x 13' 1"
DINING	12' 6" x 13' 9"
SUN LOUNGE	12' 10" x 16' 1"
BED 1	11' 6" x 16' 5"
BED 2	11' 2" x 11' 2"
BED 3	11' 2" x 11' 2"
LENGTH	58' 11"
FLOOR AREA	1803 sq. ft.

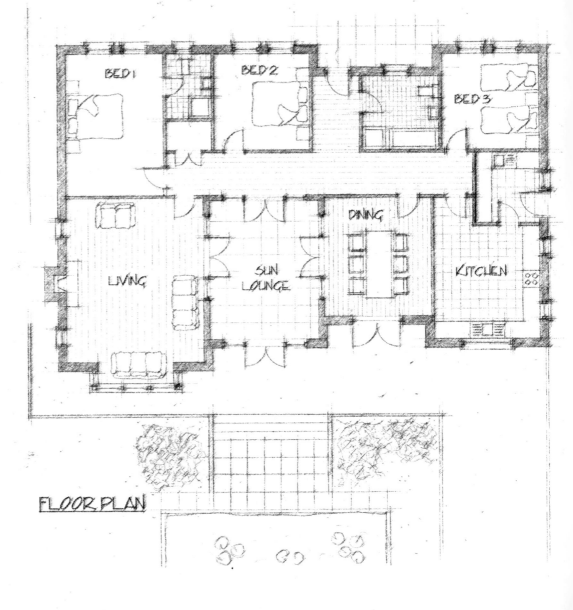

FLOOR PLAN

76

Leamareha

Arguably the most modern design of this eclectic publication, the floor plan is quartered by 2 massive cross walls which allow the architect to address differing room functions with different geometric solutions.

As with most designs, site location is critical. In reality the site is a primary dictator of the final design.

(continued over leaf)

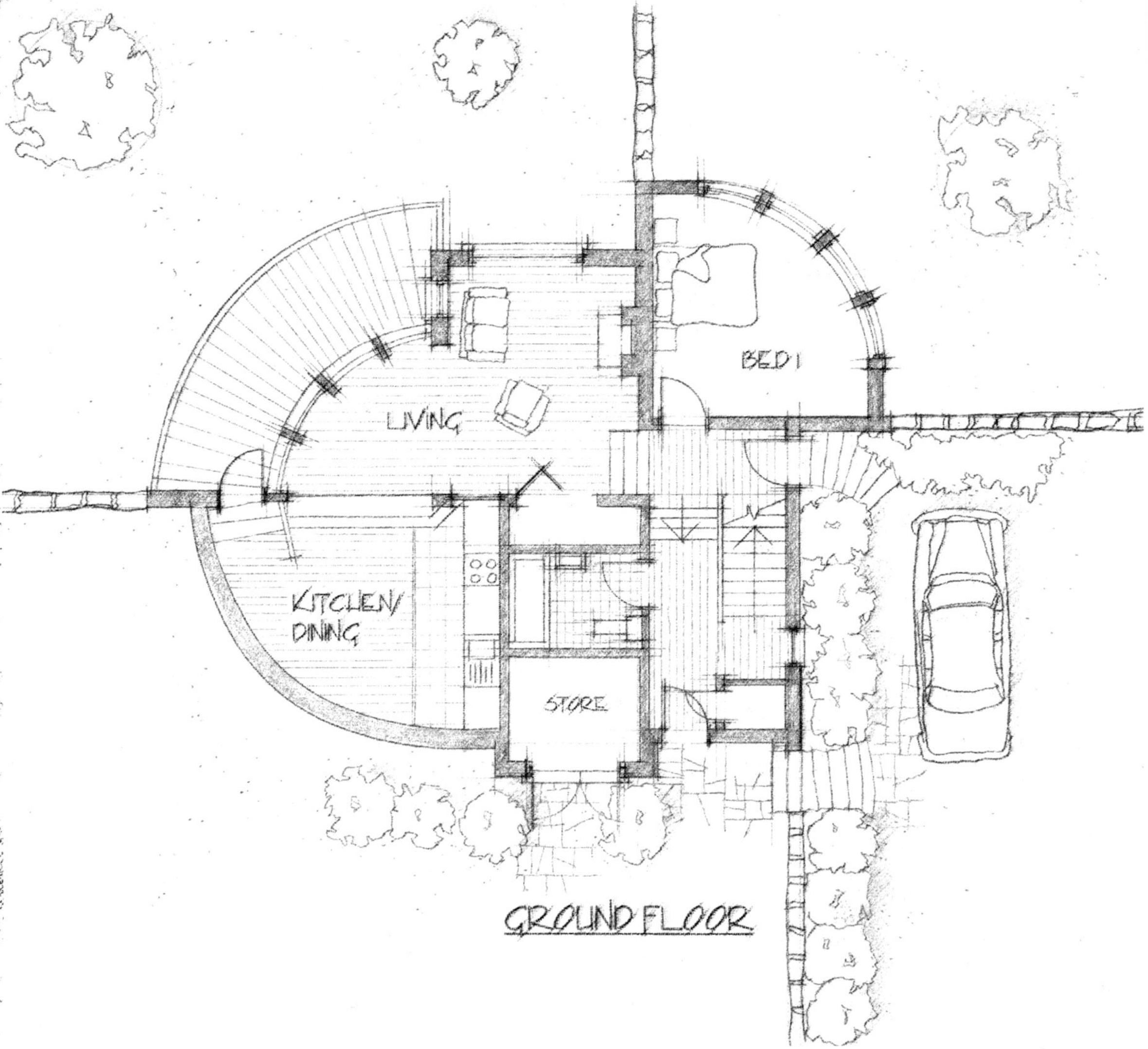

DIMENSIONS & AREAS

LIVING	22' 11" x 14' 5"
KITCHEN/DINING	18' 0" x 14' 9"
BED 1	13' 9" x 13' 9"
LENGTH	47' 3"
FLOOR AREA	1150 sq. ft.

BED 1

LIVING

KITCHEN/ DINING

STORE

GROUND FLOOR

Leamareha

(continued from previous page)

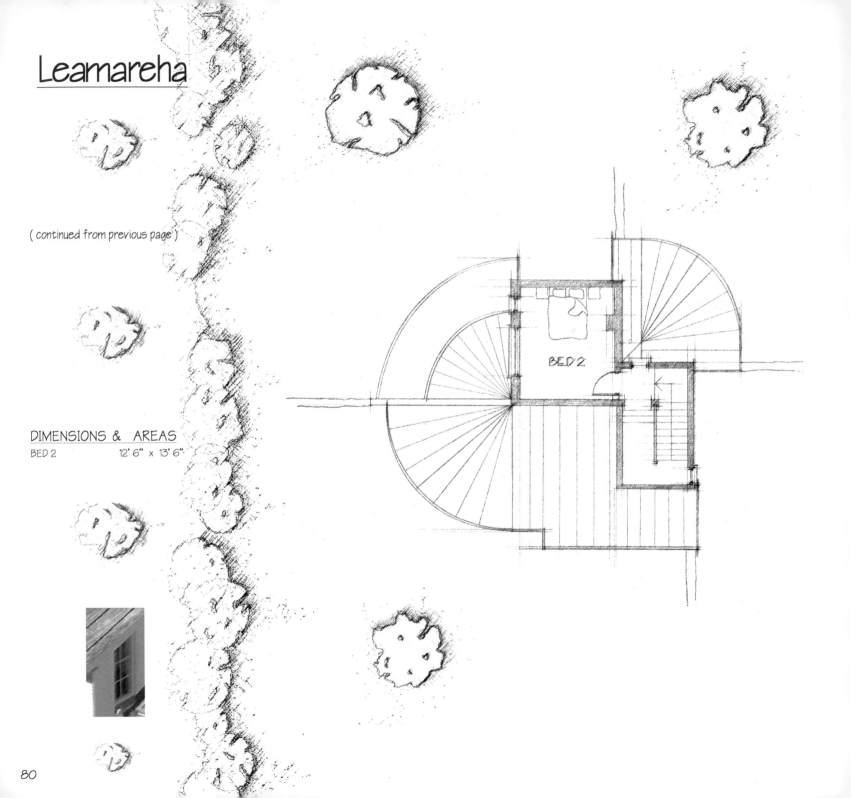

DIMENSIONS & AREAS
BED 2   12' 6" x 13' 6"

BED 2

Scanlon's

This delightful open plan dwelling is ideally suited for a south west facing site. It can be sited as a front or rear entry house.

The split level between the living room and lounge, together with the corner fireplace offer definition to each area allowing a change in character to define each space.

DIMENSIONS & AREAS

LIVING	14' 3" x 15' 11"
KITCHEN	15' 7" x 13' 9"
LOUNGE	13' 5" x 12' 11"
BED 1	15' 5" x 12' 8"
BED 2	13' 5" x 14' 7"
BED 3	10' 8" x 12' 8"
BED 4	15' 7" x 13' 9"
LENGTH	45' 5"
FLOOR AREA	2310 sq. ft.

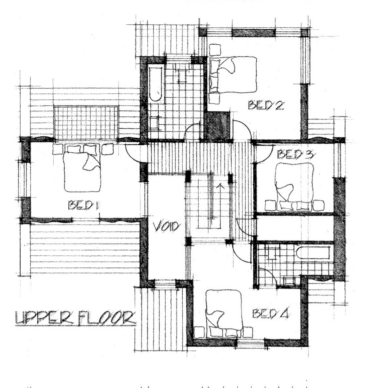

UPPER FLOOR

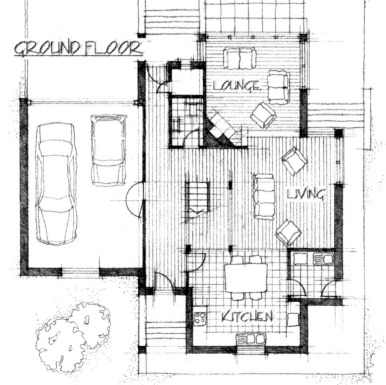

GROUND FLOOR

Gola

S tyled on a 19th Century gatehouse with very ornate bargeboards and stone finish. Natural daylight will flood the sun lounge (which should be south facing) and spill out into the kitchen and dining area.

The tiled roof finish with its terracotta banding provides further interest to this design.

DIMENSIONS & AREAS

LIVING	17' 9" x 11' 10"
KITCHEN/DINING	14' 9" x 15' 5"
SUN LOUNGE	5' 3" x 17' 9"
BED 1	19' 7" x 11' 7"
BED 2	13' 6" x 11' 10"
LENGTH	32' 10"
FLOOR AREA	1229 sq. ft.

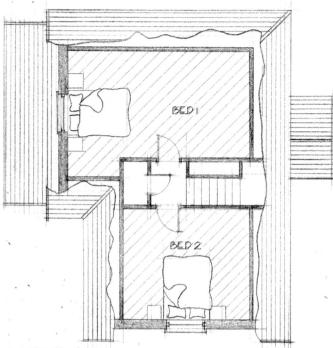

UPPER FLOOR

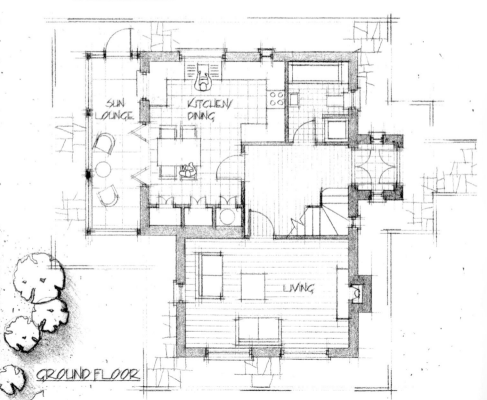

GROUND FLOOR

Castle

The siting of a lounge on the upper floor will afford the occupants of this house much greater views than those of the ground floor living area. The circular bays will act as sun traps and provide secluded restful areas on stressful days.

A little excitement is added internally with curved walls and a castle style spiral stair.

The window over the main door was inspired by the three spirals celtic symbol.

DIMENSIONS & AREAS

LIVING	19' 6" x 11' 4"
KITCHEN	12' 2" x 12' 11"
DINING	13' 7" x 12' 11"
LOUNGE	19' 6" x 11' 4"
BED 1	13' 7" x 12' 11"
BED 2	12' 2" x 12' 11"
LENGTH	41' 08"
FLOOR AREA	1770 sq. ft.

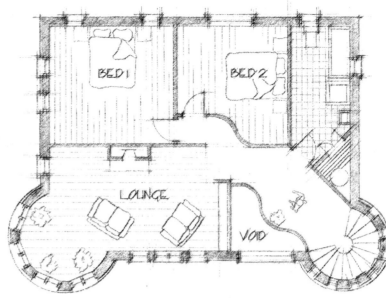

UPPER FLOOR

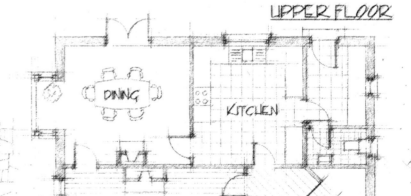

GROUND FLOOR

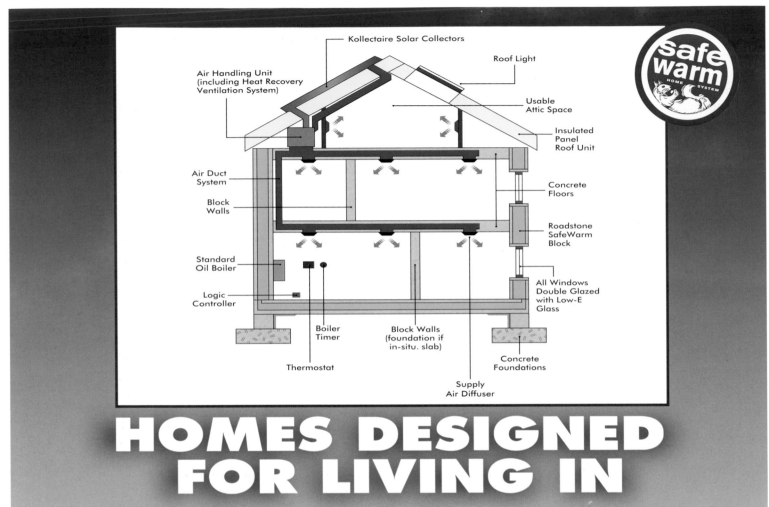

Kollectaire Solar Collectors

Air Handling Unit (including Heat Recovery Ventilation System)

Roof Light

Usable Attic Space

Insulated Panel Roof Unit

Air Duct System

Concrete Floors

Block Walls

Roadstone SafeWarm Block

Standard Oil Boiler

All Windows Double Glazed with Low-E Glass

Logic Controller

Boiler Timer

Block Walls (foundation if in-situ. slab)

Thermostat

Concrete Foundations

Supply Air Diffuser

HOMES DESIGNED FOR LIVING IN

COMFORT IS A SAFE WARM HOME

The superior specification of the SafeWarm Home system ensures real benefits

- Always comfortable; like Summer all year round
- Noise is reduced by half; concrete floors and block walls
- Healthy to live in; fresh filtered air, controlled ventilation and humidity
- Environmentally friendly; solar heating and heat recovery
- Economically more spacious with greater freedom for interior design and layout
- Lowest fuel bills; no other building system in Ireland gives lower energy costs

FOR FURTHER INFORMATION AND TECHNICAL DETAILS PLEASE CONTACT:
ROADSTONE DUBLIN LTD., FORTUNESTOWN, DUBLIN 24.
TELEPHONE 01 404 1200.   FACSIMILE 01 404 1362.

roadstone

SafeWarm Homes   *"Designed for living in"*

Comfort is a SafeWarm Home.

Once in a generation something really different is offered. In the last generation of houses it was central heating. Today it is the Roadstone SafeWarm Home system.

SafeWarm Homes are
(1) always comfortable.
(2) quiet and durable.
(3) healthy to live in.
(4) environmentally friendly.
(5) more spacious and they give greater freedom for interior design and layout.
(6) use up to 85% less oil or gas.

Roadstone, is promising all these features with their SafeWarm Home system.

These features give the benefits which we would all like to have in the home whether we are building, buying or selling.

Summer all year round.

A comfortable temperature throughout the whole house is marvellous, no cold damp rooms, every room can be used, its like summer all year round.

The quiet life.

Noise is uncomfortable and tiring and there is a huge benefit in dramatically reducing noise from one room to another and from one floor to another. There is a good feeling knowing that the house is built with traditional concrete materials proven to be rugged, safe, fireproof and built to last.

Healthy fresh air.

Ventilation means supplying fresh air into a house. Poor ventilation in a house causes humidity, stale air and an atmosphere suitable for dust mite growth. This can lead to asthma and other health problems. Draught proofing and air-tightening a house without addressing the ventilation question can make these problems worse, The feeling of living in a warm and well ventilated house with a constant supply of healthy flesh air has to be experienced to be believed. Knowing that the ventilation is not causing a major energy drain is even more comforting.

Solar heating in Ireland ?

Most people think would think Ireland does not receive a large amount of solar radiation. In fact we get 66% of what the French Riviera gets!

We can use this free solar energy to cut our heating costs and to minimize the damage we do to the enviroment.

Curtains down to the floor.

The scope for interior design and furniture arrangement is tremendous when radiators are not required. Curtains can be brought down to the floor, the piano can go on any wall.

Changing room-layout as family develops.

Using a flooring system that does not depend for support on interior walls in a house gives the householder the option of changing the interior layout of rooms as the family develops, no fears of knocking down 'structural walls'.

More space.

Ireland and the U.K, are probably unique in ignoring the option of using the roof space for general living areas. Over 300 sq ft. approximately can be built in the attic, in a 4 bed. semi-detached house, thanks to the clever design of the roof and the 2nd floor in the SafeWarm system. This extra space is in most cases the biggest room in the house.

How is all this done ?

The beauty is that it is simple; an integrated approach using:

Effective insulation with air-tightening (to half the heat losses).
Free solar energy   (to supply the bulk of the energy).
Mechanical ventilation and air filtering (to give a fresh healthy atmosphere and to control the air changes).
Heat recovery (to extract the heat from air leaving the house).
Concrete floors and concrete block walls internally (to give balanced thermal capacity necessary for heat storage and to cut down on noise).
Automatic controls and a back-up boiler (to control temperatures, to avoid waste and to supply energy when there is no solar available).

Summary

The combination of high levels of effective insulation, air-tightening, controlled ventilation with heat recovery, high thermal capacity and a free (solar) energy supply forms the basis of the Roadstone SafeWarm Home system and can be incorporated into virtually any house design.

For further information please contact Roadstone **Dublin,**
Tel 01 4041200
Fax 01 4041362

Clare

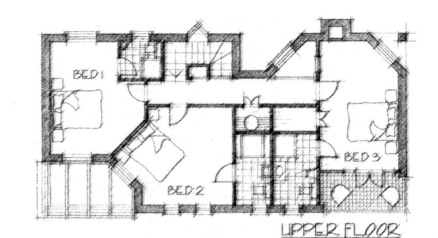

For a relatively large house, over 1800 sq. ft. there are a surprising number of wee niches within; the sun lounge and dining area on the ground floor, the private balcony off the master bedroom and the small void looking down into the lounge on the upper floor.

The large bedrooms also benefit from en-suite facilities.

DIMENSIONS & AREAS

LIVING	21' 11" x 8' 3"
KITCHEN	12' 2" x 9' 4"
LOUNGE	21' 11" x 13' 3"
SUN LOUNGE	11' 3" x 5' 9"
BED 1	12' 9" x 14' 11"
BED 2	10' 9" x 17' 1"
BED 3	12' 2" x 12' 11"
LENGTH	48' 7"
FLOOR AREA	1832 sq. ft.

UPPER FLOOR

GROUND FLOOR

Eeshal

A subtle use of differing materials and the feature curved front wall combine to give this house a classic well proportioned front facade with single and two storey sections. The internal layout exploits both the winter and summer daylight with a double height living room, with huge glazing areas, and a smaller more intimate winter room.

DIMENSIONS & AREAS

LIVING	14' 3" x 20' 2"
KITCHEN	16' 5" x 15' 7"
LOUNGE	21' 11" x 13' 3"
WINTER ROOM	6' 7" Diammeter
PLAYROOM	13' 2" x 8'
BED 1	10' 2" x 12' 10"
BED 2	13' 5" x 15' 8"
BED 3	13' 5" x 12' 2"
LENGTH	61'
FLOOR AREA	2425 sq. ft.

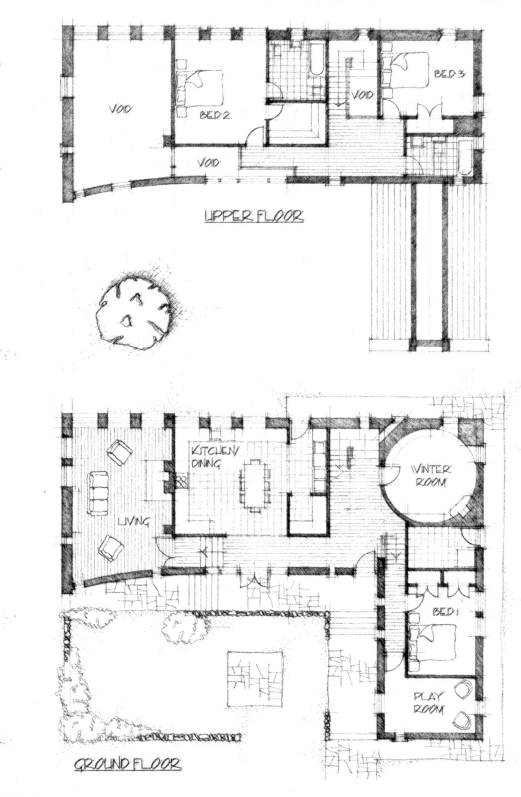

UPPER FLOOR

GROUND FLOOR

Fiddoun

Featured on the front cover, the raised eaves give this design an simple elegance,

Internally the large open hallway is almost an extra room. Full height shelving envelops the staircase and provides for those essential holiday accessories - games, toys, CD's and books.

The first floor landing is softly lit by way of the feature bullseye window.

DIMENSIONS & AREAS

LIVING	13' 1" x 19' 8"
KITCHEN	13' 1" x 19' 8"
BED 1	13' 1" x 12' 9"
BED 2	13' 1" x 12' 9"
LENGTH	41' 4"
FLOOR AREA	1380 sq. ft.

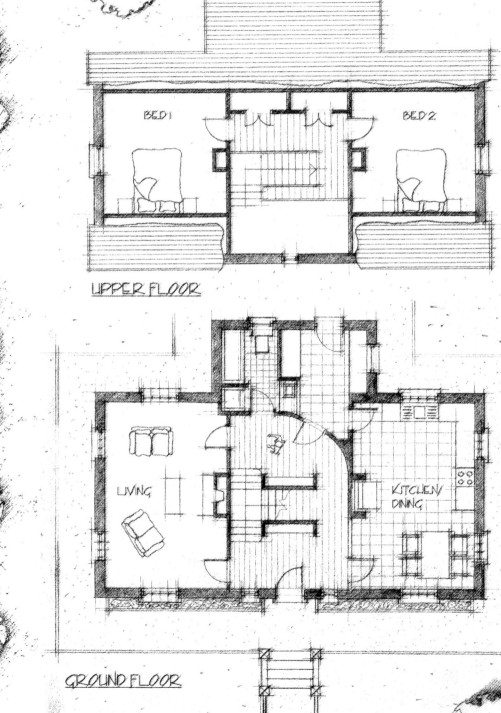

UPPER FLOOR

BED 1

BED 2

GROUND FLOOR

LIVING

KITCHEN/ DINING

Rathlin O'Byrne

This one bedroom cottage, easily the smallest in the book, has been specifically designed to provide adequate holiday accommodation at minimal cost.

It could however be altered and extended by the addition of an area, equivalent to the living room, to the right gable wall thus creating a symmetrical floor plan.

DIMENSIONS & AREAS

LIVING/DINING	12' 6" x 19' 8"
KITCHEN	9' 2" x 14' 1"
BED 1	10' 10" x 14' 1"
LENGTH	41' 0"
FLOOR AREA	637 sq. ft.

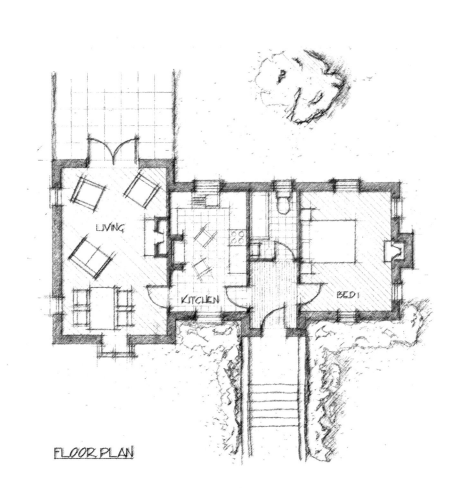

FLOOR PLAN

Aughinish

A traditional two storey thatched house with a single storey addition to one end. There is a porch entrance to both the front and back, over which is located the main bathroom.

The master bedroom has the luxury of an en-suite in a break from traditional planning.

The heart of the house is the kitchen and the heart of the kitchen is the range.

DIMENSIONS & AREAS

LIVING	13' 1" x 16' 5"
KITCHEN/DINING	14' 9" x 16' 5"
LOUNGE	14' 9" x 16' 5"
BED 1	14' 9" x 16' 5"
BED 2	14' 9" x 9' 0"
BED 3	14' 9" x 7' 1"
LENGTH	52' 10"
FLOOR AREA	1540 sq. ft.

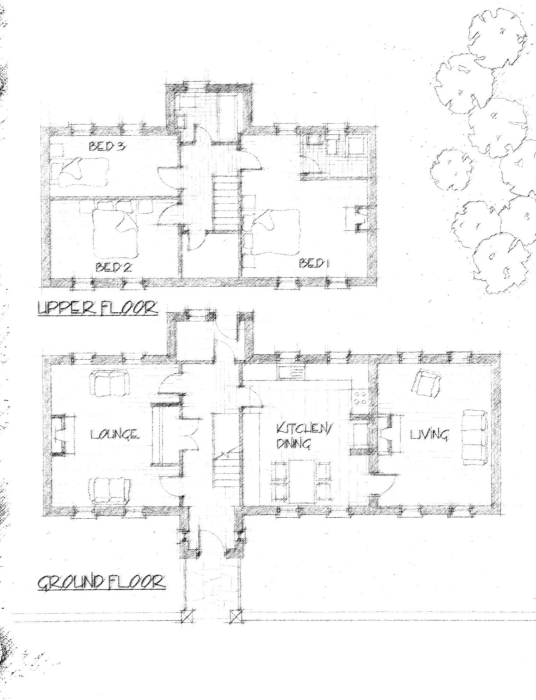

UPPER FLOOR

BED 3 BED 2 BED 1

GROUND FLOOR

LOUNGE KITCHEN/DINING LIVING

HALLMARK WALLING – THE ALTERNATIVE TO NATURAL STONE OR BRICKWORK

The use of natural stone and brickwork has been with us for many centuries; its durability and aesthetic appeal ensures their continued use in modern day construction.

Natural stone is an expensive form of construction, often difficult to source and very labour intensive. It requires the skills of a stone mason, and must be hand picked to achieve the desired effect.

Roadstone with its policy of constant product innovation has developed the Hallmark range of walling, which is the ideal alternative to Natural stone, at a fraction of the cost and is seen by many as a welcome change for the all "too standard" clay brick. Hallmark Walling, unlike natural stone is available ex stock and can easily be laid by a bricklayer.

Hallmark can be built using different bond patterns including random bond, coursed bond and random brought to course, thus allowing the flexibility to give any house or housing development a unique appearance.

The success of Hallmark walling can be illustrated by its presence in almost every county throughout Ireland. It is particularly suited to areas where planning considerations call for extra sensitivity. Its ability to merge easily with beautiful surroundings or traditional architecture can contribute enormously to the local environment.

The use of contrasting coloured mortars combined with the seven different colours in the Hallmark range is a very important consideration, as this can have a significant effect on the overall appearance. Joints can be finished flush, tooled or bagged depending on the overall effect required and local custom. Recessed joints are not recommended.

Cottage: Colour - Silver

Bungalow: Colour - Pewter

On a practical level it is built using standard cavity wall construction and can be easily combined with brickwork or render. This is beautifully illustrated below – Here Hallmark Pewter Blend in random bond is complemented by an Ormonde "Orchard Wall" clay brick in a private residence in Waterford. This is just one of many beautiful examples of its use.

Quoin stones (corner blocks) in either smooth or a textured finish are available to compliment the range of colours. Although they are not necessary for the construction, they are an attractive feature and can enhance and add character to any house.

Hallmark walling is available nation-wide and is accompanied by a county-wide technical backup service for your convenience.

Why not call us for a full colour brochure to see for yourself the flexibility, versatility and beauty of Hallmark walling as used in a variety of projects which will convince you that Hallmark Walling is the modern day alternative to brickwork and expensive stonework.

Contact us at :
Roadstone Architectural Products Division
Huntstown, North Road
Finglas, Dublin 11
Phone 01-8343322 Fax   01-8343931

Corner Detail: Colour - Pewter

Computer Image: Colour - Pewter

Inishdalla

B ased on a contemporary design, this dwelling has an open plan living and dining area maximising on the natural sunlight.

The overhanging roof highlights the entrance with a covered balcony available from all three bedrooms at first floor level.

A combination of external wall and roof finishes results in a very individual image.

(continued over leaf).

DIMENSIONS & AREAS

LIVING	16' 9" x 20' 4"
DINING	13' 9" x 9' 10"
KITCHEN	11' 6" x 13' 2"
LENGTH	52' 2"
FLOOR AREA	2055 sq. ft.

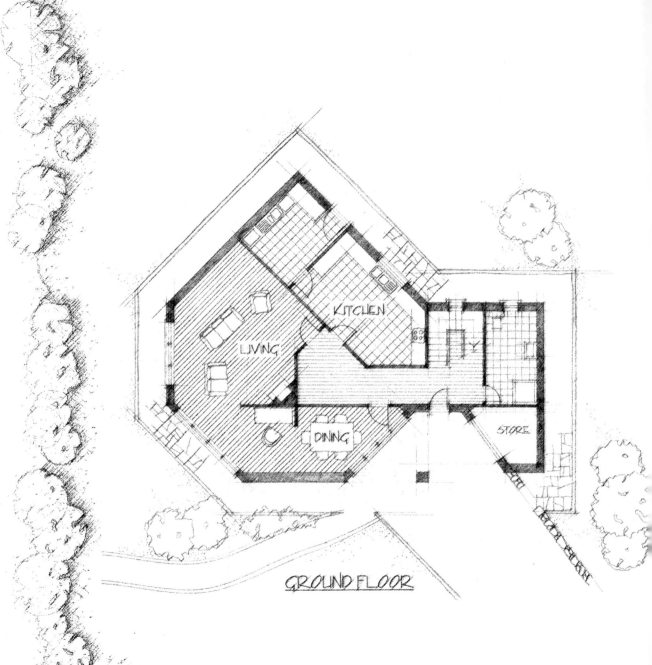

KITCHEN

LIVING

DINING

STORE

GROUND FLOOR

103

Inishdalla

(continued from previous page).

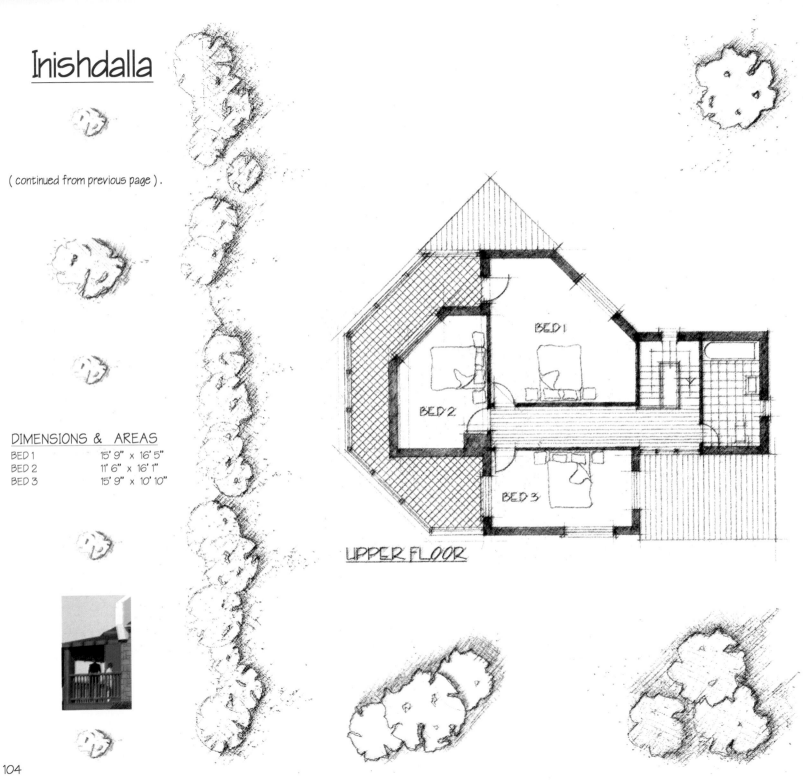

DIMENSIONS & AREAS
BED 1	15' 9" x 16' 5"
BED 2	11' 6" x 16' 1"
BED 3	15' 9" x 10' 10"

BED 1

BED 2

BED 3

UPPER FLOOR

Light House

T his house was designed for sites with an excessive slope.
The main living and sleeping apartments are arranged on three levels within the square block, with the entrance and ancillary accommodation attached to the other end of the circulation stair.
Although the design is modern in approach, traditional concepts of private space are maintained and the focal point of the living space remains the large fireplace.

(continued over leaf).

DIMENSIONS & AREAS

LOUNGE	18' 1" x 18' 1"
BED 1	12' 10" x 9' 10"
LENGTH	47' 3"
FLOOR AREA	1522 sq. ft.

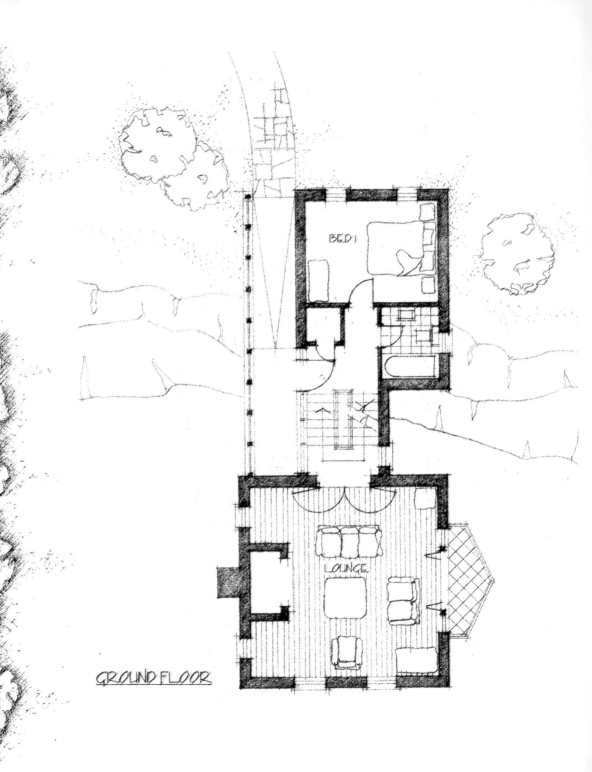

BED 1

LOUNGE

GROUND FLOOR

Light House

(continued from previous page).

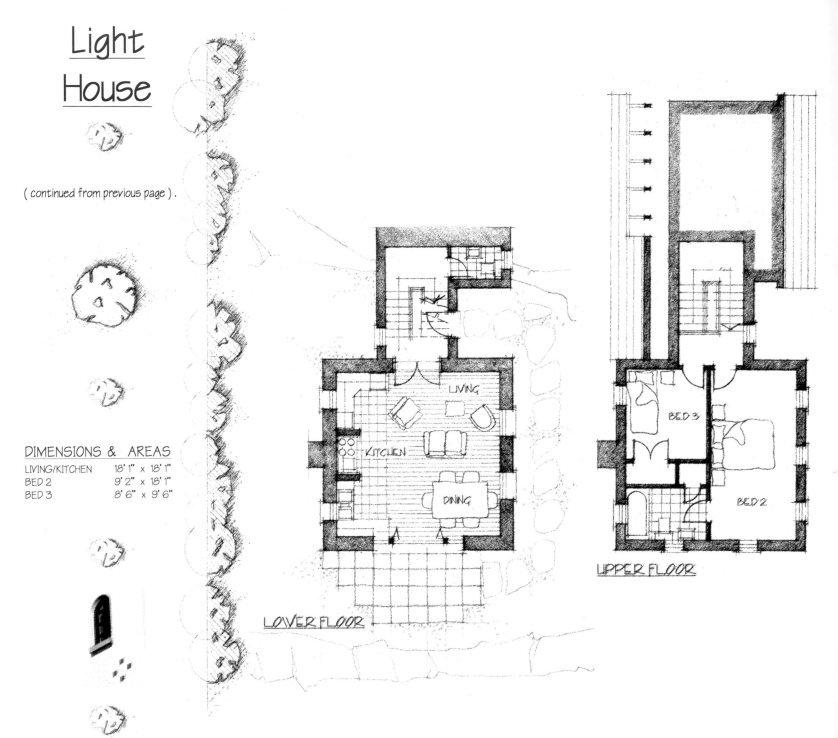

DIMENSIONS & AREAS

LIVING/KITCHEN	18' 1" x 18' 1"
BED 2	9' 2" x 18' 1"
BED 3	8' 6" x 9' 6"

LIVING

KITCHEN

DINING

LOWER FLOOR

BED 3

BED 2

UPPER FLOOR

Irishmuskerry

This design was inspired by an old hunting lodge in the highlands of Scotland but is intended here for less aggressive pastimes.

The living room has windows in all four walls affording almost panoramic vision.

The large first floor balcony is intended for balmy evenings and post prandial drinks.

DIMENSIONS & AREAS

LIVING	10' 10" x 19' 8"
KITCHEN/DINING	10' 10" x 19' 8"
BED 1	10' 10" x 19' 8"
BED 2	10' 10" x 19' 8"
LENGTH	38' 5"
FLOOR AREA	1244 sq. ft.

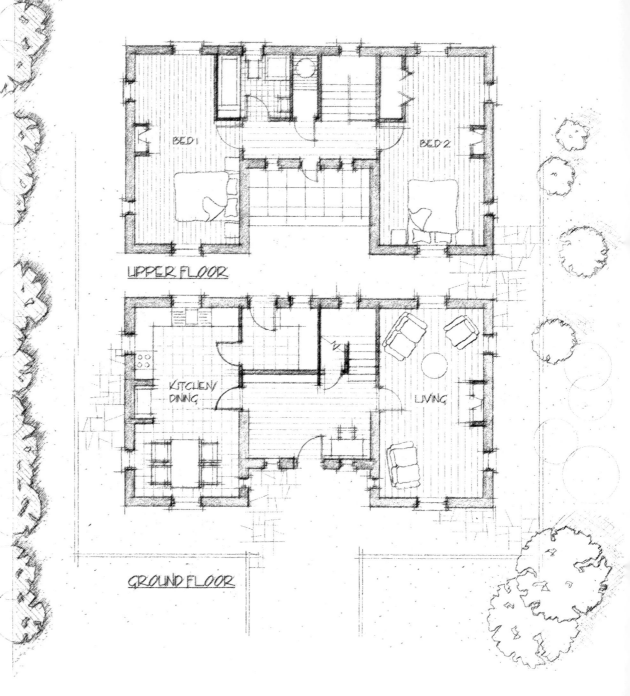

UPPER FLOOR

GROUND FLOOR

Inishbarra

A central atrium floods the heart of this house with daylight. A combination of single and two storey, the living area enjoys the extra height of a vaulted roof whilst the central staircase forms a strong image opposite. The main entrance gives a dramatic ascent to the first floor.

(continued over leaf)

DIMENSIONS & AREAS

LIVING	17' 8" x 13' 6"
KITCHEN/DINING	11' 6" x 13' 9"
LOUNGE	21' 4" x 12' 10"
BED 1	14' 1" x 13' 1"
LENGTH	56' 9"
FLOOR AREA	1850 sq. ft.

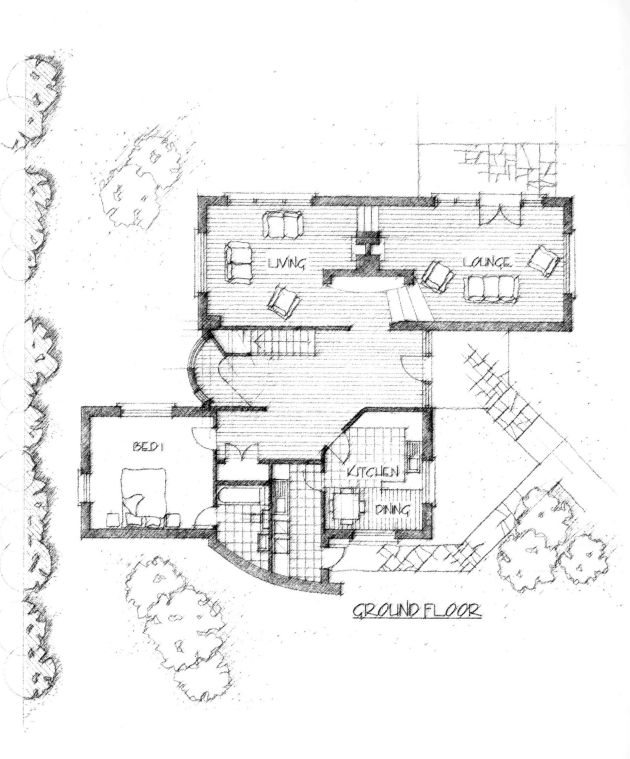

GROUND FLOOR

Inishbarra

(continued from previous page)

DIMENSIONS & AREAS

BED 2	14' 1" x 13' 1"
BED 3	11' 6" x 13' 1"

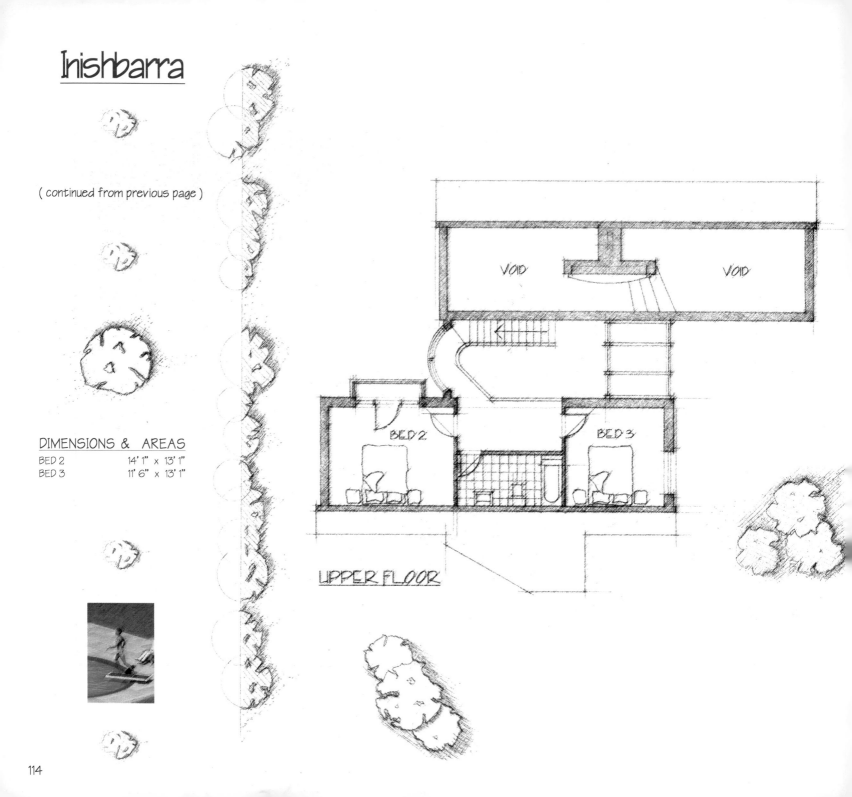

VOID

VOID

BED 2

BED 3

UPPER FLOOR

BEDROOMS

All bedrooms should be different to reflect the differing needs and aspirations of the individual user. There is no limit to what uses a bedroom may have or indeed as to where the bedroom may be located.

In some instances the bedroom is located at the top of the house to optimise the availability of daylight, and in others it may be at ground level to optimise the access to the garden and external areas. In your consideration of a suitable location for the bedroom many factors come into play including the need to be near the bathroom, children's bedroom or readily accessible to the balcony.

The design of the bedroom offers you an opportunity to create a semi-private space where you can indulge your imagination and satisfy your physical needs for quiet undisturbed sleep while at the same time providing a haven for personal contemplative reflection.

The primary function of a bedroom is for sleeping, waking and starting the day. The dominant feature of the room should therefore be the bed. By establishing the type of bed, whether it be existing or new, you will form a clear picture of the layout, mood and size of the bedroom at an early stage of the house design development. Further consideration for the room may include whether it would be required to double as a work space, study or gym etc. By developing an early understanding of the physical functional and spatial requirements of the house such questions as regards bedroom sizes and locations can be quickly incorporated in the context of overall house design. Lighting within bedrooms is primarily provided by either natural early morning light or artificial light by night. Ideally the bedroom should be orientated to the Irish climate, to the East and South-East corner of the site, to maximize the availability of natural light within the room. Bedrooms are occupied primarily at night and as such artificial light will be used for a significant period of the time.

Artificial light in bedrooms is required in a similar fashion as the lighting in kitchens and offices, it being necessary to cater for a variety of different functions ranging from general background light, task lights for dressing and applying make-up, reading lights located at the bed-head, to spot lights for highlighting important decorative features or items of furniture.

The decoration and design of the bedroom play a very important role in developing the mood of the room. Colours such as pure white may be used to enhance limited natural sunlight in wintertime or to reflect artificial light while darker brown or green could be used to mute the light and thus create a more intimate mood.

The ceiling finish in the bedroom, unlike many other rooms, should be given more consideration than is usually the case as the main vantage point for viewing the bedroom is from the horizontal position. This also reminds us that there may be elements of the room that may need to be arranged so as to be viewed from the bed - for example window cill heights may be dropped or roof-lights located above the bed-head and other items of furniture arranged to be easily accessible from the bed.

Children's bedrooms will change radically as the children grow. A child's bedroom may start out as toddler's nursery and develop into a private teenage den used for "hanging out", listening to music and entertaining friends. The bedroom, irrespective of child's age, should offer a stimulating safe environment in which a quite considerable period of a child's home life might be spent. Children's rooms will be required to fit a number of functions ranging from sleeping to studying and playing.

Particular attention should be paid to storage in children's bedrooms. This could allow exciting spaces to be created when combined with other functions of the room.

Floors to bedrooms should be smooth and soft. Even where a hard surface such as timber or tiles is proposed it would be prudent to soften these surfaces with large rugs and mats. It should be noted that carpets within bedrooms are not subject to the same degree of wear as those in hall or living room areas and therefore the most expensive quality of carpet is not a necessity.

Furniture in bedrooms is crucially important as bedrooms often tend to untidiness and therefore provision of adequate storage is important. Storage space may be provided by built-in cupboards or ready-made wardrobes. Storage should be allowed for a number of objects of different sizes from shoes to coats.
Built-in dressing room and en-suites may be included if space allows. There are no set dimensions for these spaces as sizes can range from that of a small wardrobe to an average size room and larger.

BATHROOMS

The average sized bathroom in Ireland today is just 6ft x 9ft. This, of course, includes all existing stock, with the smaller bathrooms being found in the speculative semi-detached market.

There are many important factors to be taken into account when attempting to get the bathroom right. For a room which has, traditionally, been designed as the smallest room in the house, its duties, functions and responsibilities can be a heavy weight on its often meagre shoulders.

Of all the aspects to a bathroom which must be considered the two which stand out as being most crucial are location and comfort.

The bathroom must be located so that it is readily accessible to all the people who wish to use it. This will vary considerably depending on the number of bathrooms which are to be constructed within the dwelling. In modern dwellings it would be very unusual to have just one bathroom. It would now be considered normal that at least the master bedroom would have its own private bathroom or en-suite. In a large dwelling of five bedrooms or more a second en-suite should be considered, allowing the three remaining rooms to share the main bathroom. Another aspect which must be considered is whether or not the main bathroom will be utilised for general daily use or if a separate w.c. is available. Often a w.c. will be located to the rear of a dwelling - accessed from a utility room This can be particularly useful for children playing outside - avoiding the need for pulling buckets of sand, mud and other undesirables through the house in times of emergency. In a two-story dwelling a dilemma often arises. One wants to be able to facilitate visitors by having a w.c. on the ground floor. However, if this w.c. is accessed from a utility or back hall for reasons described above, one may be reluctant to send visitors into this area. In this situation it is more prudent to consider the general needs of the family. Visitors are usually more than happy to use a first floor bathroom which is likely to be the bathroom into which most thought and expense has gone. Finally don't think of the bathroom as simply a place to take care of hygiene needs. Enjoy the room and the atmosphere which can be created therein.

The second item we must consider in the bathroom is comfort. This will mean different things to different people and take in items such as layout, heating and decor.

When designing a bathroom - particularly on the first floor - thought must be given to the position and direction of services. Appliances should, ideally, be positioned so that drainage can now run in the same direction as floor joists. Where this is not feasible raised areas within the bathroom can be considered. These can be an attractive feature while at the same time hiding pipework.

Because the bathroom can be an expensive room to fit out, it is important to get the layout right. This is doubly the case when one considers that once appliances are fixed, they cannot be readily relocated.

Traditionally baths were located on one wall with the w.c., wash hand basin and possibly bidet on another. Bathroom layout is now moving on and where space allows it is not uncommon to position the bath in the centre of the room. Here an antique or reproduction bath can form the main focus possibly on a raised platform within the room. Alternatively, and if the house design allows, the bath can be sunk into the floor. Should the height not be available in the floor below, a similar effect can be created by providing steps up to a raised area into which the bath is recessed.

It must be considered whether or not a separate shower is required within a bathroom. If space allows, this will afford greater comfort for those who prefer the convenience of a shower to a bath. The numerous fittings available including body sprays, double showers and even steam units. If space is not abundant, a shower can be fitted above the bath with either a curtain or screen surround. Again the variety of fitting available including screens and curtains for corner baths allows for maximum choice.

The type of suite chosen should, in some way, reflect the style of room one wishes to create. The bathroom is a place where, if budget permits, we can allow our imagination a free rein. With anything from great gothic indulgence to lavish Romanesque with marble floors, baths and porticos or traditional free standing claw foot roll-top bath and washed timber paneling.

Whichever style is chosen, think seriously before purchasing a suite in a strong color. It is very hard to improve on classic white which is practically guaranteed to stay in fashion.

Finishes which can be applied within a bathroom are various and the materials used are only limited by budget. Tiling has been and continues to be the most popular finish. One possible drawback with this is the costs involved if one wants a change of decor. For this reason, it may be worth considering tiling to dado height and applying a paint or paper finish above this.

Timber paneling used in times gone by is experiencing a strong revival. The paneling is usually fixed to a wall up to dado height and can be finished with a varnish, paint or wash.Granite and marble vanity tops are also quite popular at the upper end of the market. Regardless of which materials are chosen be sure they are moisture proof, never use uncoated papers, matt paints or corodable metals. Ensure any furniture, cabinets or cupboards are constructed from materials which will not suffer from exposure to moisture.

The bathroom should be well-heated. Gone are the days when bathrooms were merely used for a brisk wash at either end of the day. People are now spending more time in the bathroom and, with options such as large Jacuzzi baths, fireplaces, televisions and exercise equipment, the bathroom can be a place to unwind after a tough day, to get away from the kids or plan a romantic meeting with a little bubbly - be it Dom Perignon or Mr. Bubbles.

Heating is usually provided either by radiant or under-floor heating. On a ground floor under-floor heating is by far the most desirable. It provides an even, comfortable heat and a warm surface on which to walk. Under-floor heating can also be utilised on the first floor but it can sometimes be difficult to achieve. If radiators are used ensure they are located in positions where they will not cause burns when accidentally brushed against. Towel rail radiators can be an attractive alternative to the standard radiator. They come in a variety of styles and have obvious practical advantages.

Adam's

Best suited for a south-westerly
facing site, this house is accessed
from the rear opening up onto a large
glazed front elevation incorporating a
sun lounge.

The angled footprint offers a great
sun catchment area and increased
privacy whilst passing through the
house.

The five double bedrooms utilize the
maximum amount of roof space whilst
still allowing a balcony area over the
vaulted kitchen.

(continued over leaf)

DIMENSIONS & AREAS

LIVING	14' 6" x 17' 1"
KITCHEN/DINETTE	13' 9" x 26' 10"
LOUNGE	11' 9" x 15' 0"
DINING	12' 8" x 14' 1"
SUN LOUNGE	7' 6" x 15' 1"
LENGTH	74' 3"
FLOOR AREA	3340 sq. ft.

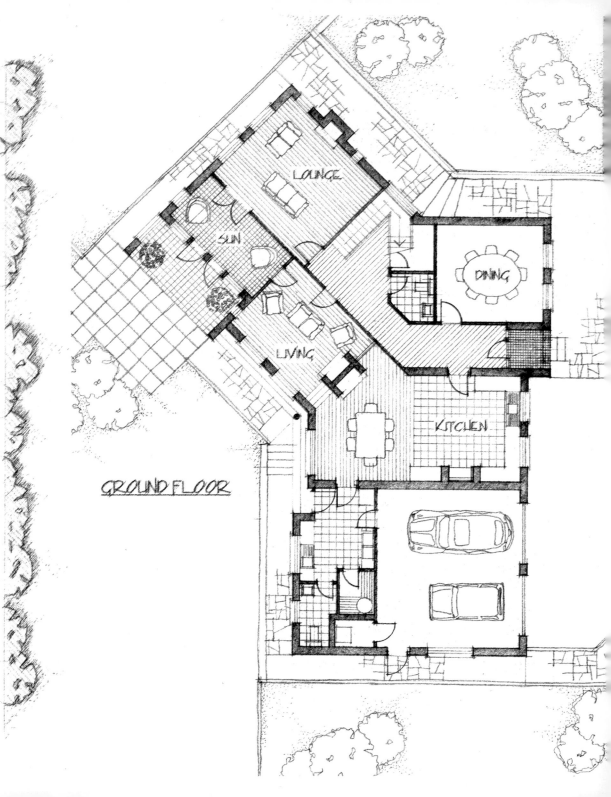

GROUND FLOOR

LOUNGE

SUN

LIVING

DINING

KITCHEN

Adam's

(continued from previous page)

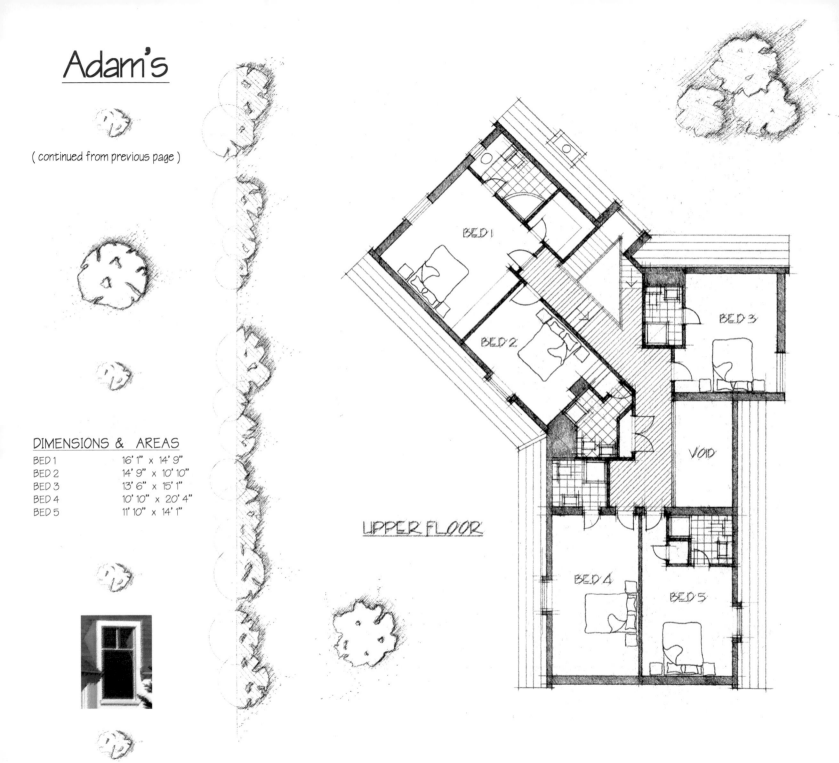

DIMENSIONS & AREAS

BED 1	16' 1" x 14' 9"
BED 2	14' 9" x 10' 10"
BED 3	13' 6" x 15' 1"
BED 4	10' 10" x 20' 4"
BED 5	11' 10" x 14' 1"

UPPER FLOOR

Eve's

The double height entrance lobby adds strength to this delightful cottage style dwelling. Despite having five bedrooms this house manages to maintain the scale of a cottage.

The combined double garage gives a defined gable frontage to complement the decreasing eaves levels of the main body of the house.

The living room has a vaulted ceiling creating a large spacious area.

(continued over leaf)

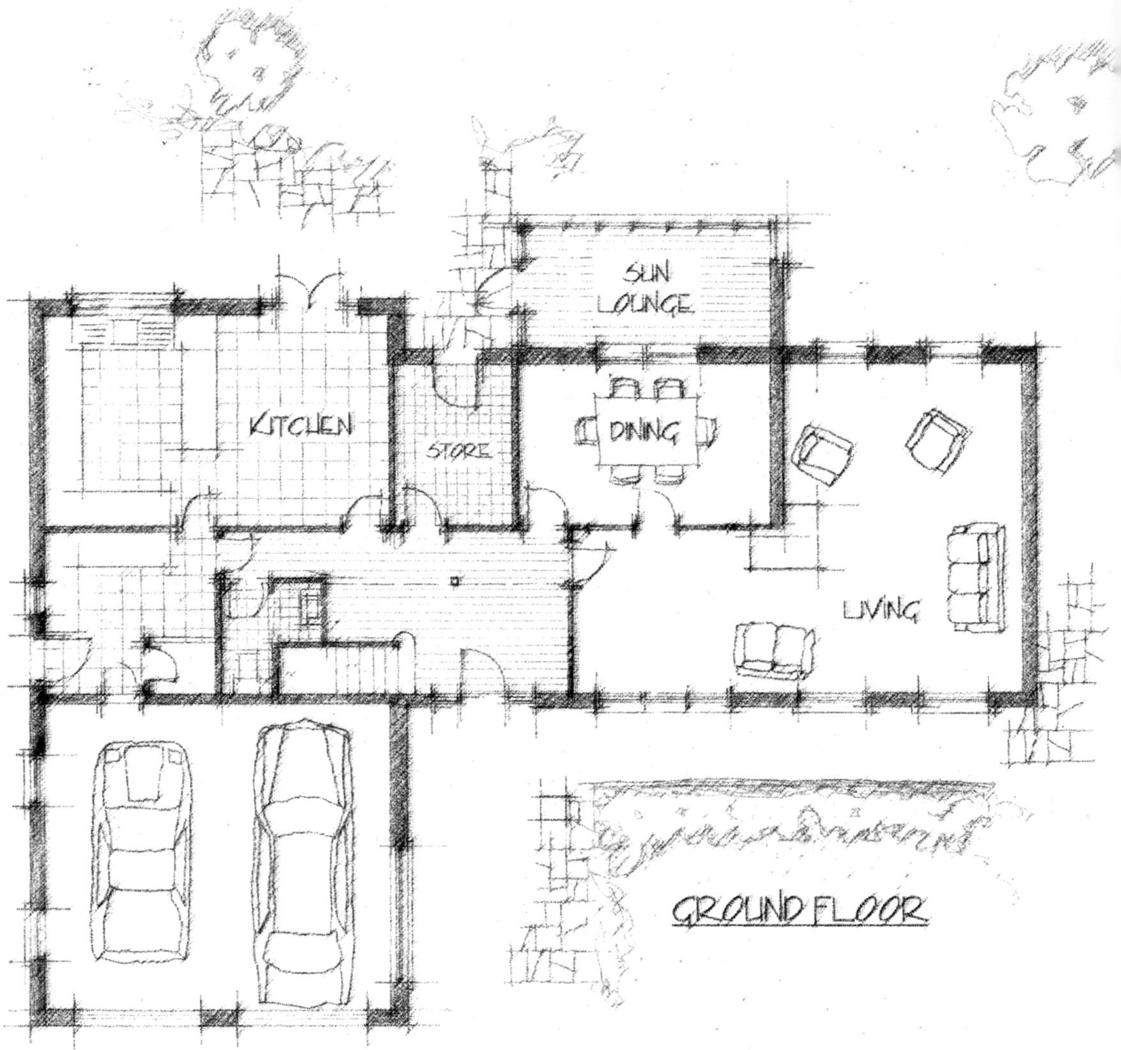

DIMENSIONS & AREAS

LIVING	19' 4" x 13' 9"
KITCHEN	20' 4" x 12' 6"
DINING	14' 9" x 9' 6"
SUN LOUNGE	10' 10" x 20' 4"
LENGTH	42' 4"
FLOOR AREA	3019 sq. ft.

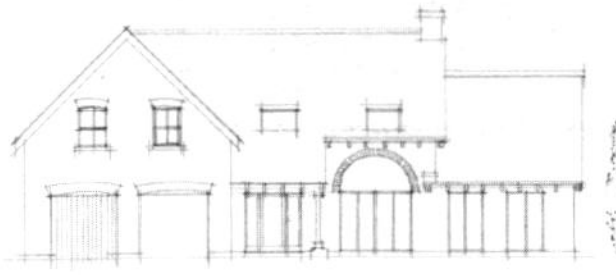

SUN LOUNGE

KITCHEN

STORE

DINING

LIVING

GROUND FLOOR

Eve's

(continued from previous page)

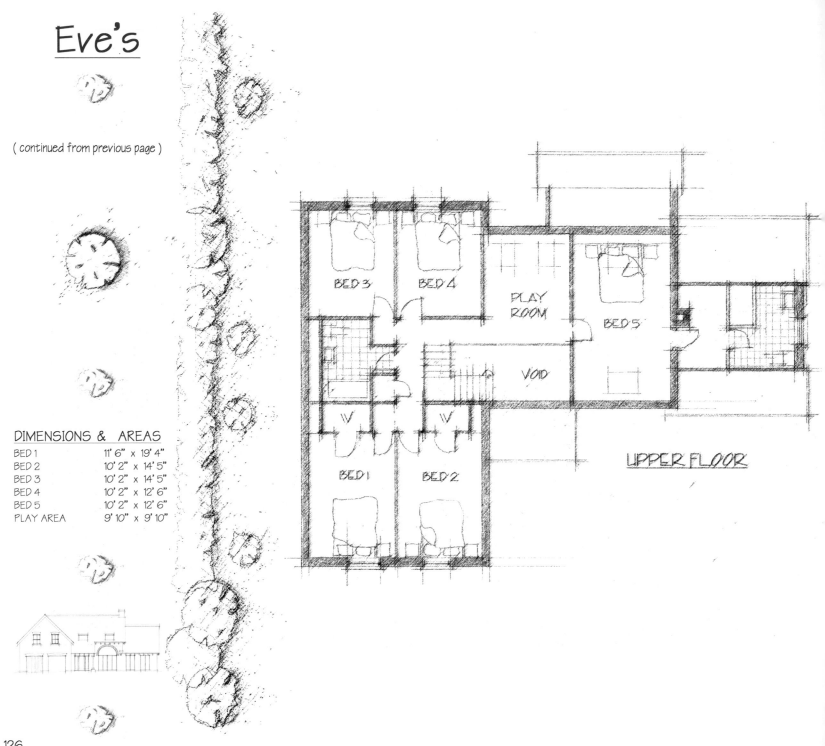

DIMENSIONS & AREAS

BED 1	11' 6" x 19' 4"
BED 2	10' 2" x 14' 5"
BED 3	10' 2" x 14' 5"
BED 4	10' 2" x 12' 6"
BED 5	10' 2" x 12' 6"
PLAY AREA	9' 10" x 9' 10"

BED 3

BED 4

PLAY ROOM

BED 5

VOID

BED 1

BED 2

UPPER FLOOR

Ballycotton

The main entrance lobby acts as a separation of the living quarters from the bedrooms. The kitchen and dining room are in a single storey vaulted section of the building whereas the bedrooms are in a dormer section.

A back courtyard offers greater definition to the rear of the site and vehicular access to the garage.

A traditionally styled cottage working on different scales and levels.

(continued over leaf)

DIMENSIONS & AREAS

LIVING	14' 3" x 18' 8"
KITCHEN	14' 3" x 9' 10"
BED 1	13' 2" x 11' 6"
BED 2	12' 2" x 11' 10"
LENGTH	59' 0"
FLOOR AREA	1850 sq. ft.

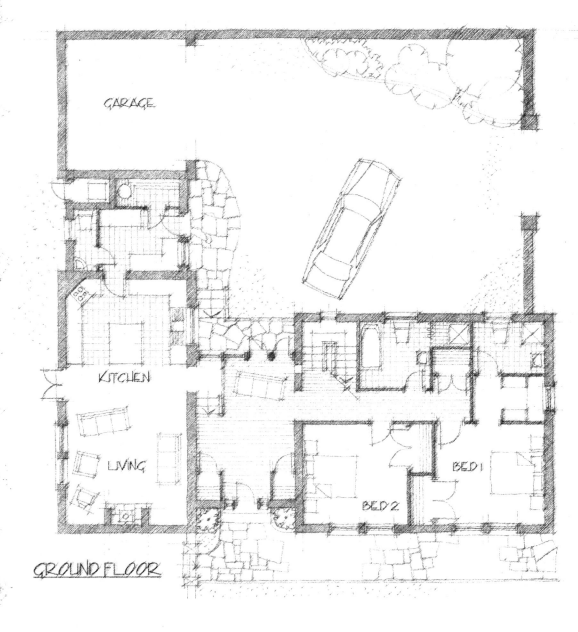

GARAGE

KITCHEN

LIVING

BED 2

BED 1

GROUND FLOOR

Ballycotton

(continued from previous page)

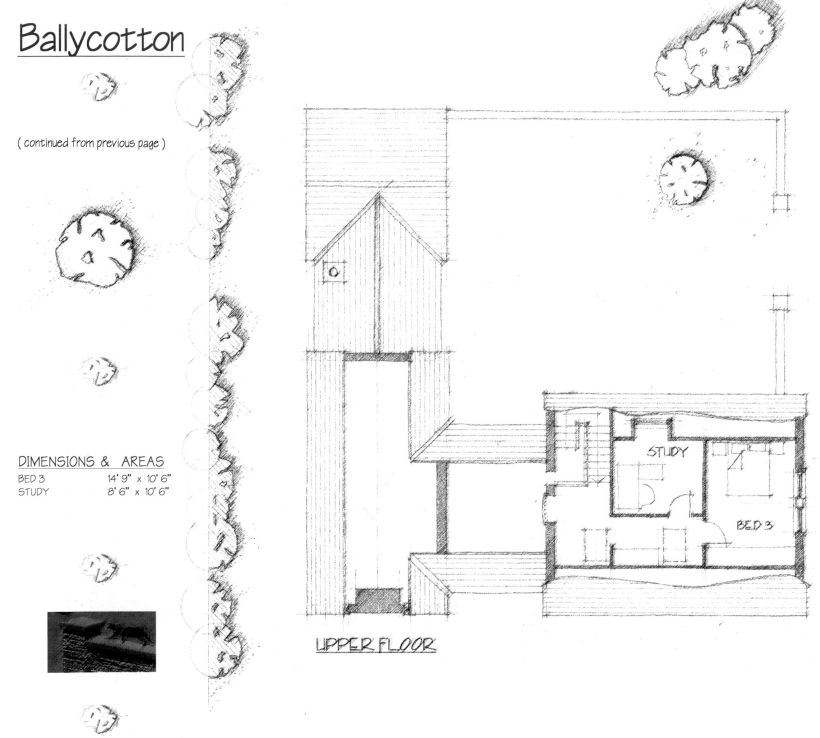

DIMENSIONS & AREAS

BED 3	14' 9" x 10' 6"
STUDY	8' 6" x 10' 6"

STUDY

BED 3

UPPER FLOOR

Saint Patrick's

The use of traditional materials to generate a development responding to the Irish countryside. This four unit development is aimed at the holiday letting market with ; a single bedroom unit, two double bedroom units and a family four bedroom unit. This refurbishment blends a mixture of traditional images with the comforts of modern inventions, illustrating the result when sensitive design is utilized to restore redundant outbuildings.

(continued over leaf)

DIMENSIONS & AREAS

UNIT 1
LIVING/KITCHEN	19' 1" x 12' 10"
BED 1	10' 10" x 12' 10"
FLOOR AREA	495 sq. ft.

UNIT 2
LIVING/KITCHEN	19' 8" x 12' 10"
BED 1	12' 2" x 12' 10"
BED 2	9' 3" x 12' 10"
FLOOR AREA	622 sq. ft.

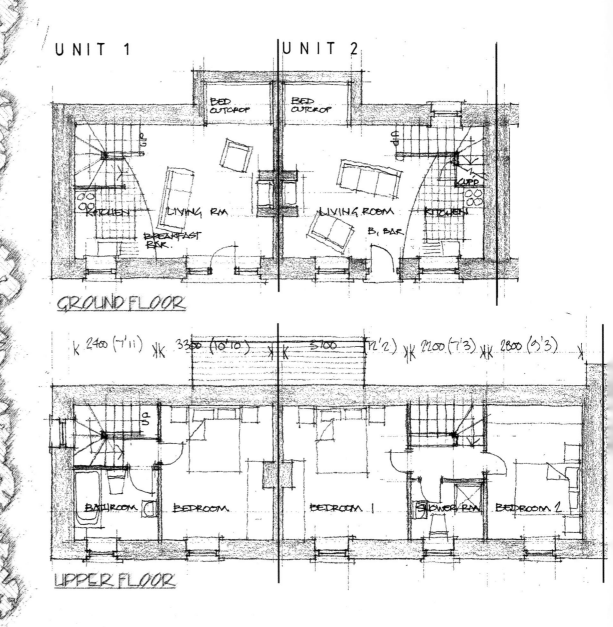

UNIT 1   UNIT 2

BED OUTCROP   BED OUTCROP

KITCHEN   LIVING RM   LIVING ROOM   KITCHEN

BREAKFAST BAR.   B. BAR

GROUND FLOOR

2400 (7'11)   3300 (10'10)   5700   (12'2)   2200 (7'3)   2800 (9'3)

BATHROOM   BEDROOM   BEDROOM 1   SHOWER RM   BEDROOM 2

UPPER FLOOR

Saint Patrick's

(continued from previous page)

DIMENSIONS & AREAS

UNIT 3
LIVING	12' 7" x 14' 10"
KITCHEN	10' 10" x 9' 2"
BED 1	11' 10" x 12' 2"
BED 2	10' 10" x 9' 2"
BED 3	11' 10" x 12' 2"
BED 4	12' 7" x 14' 7"
FLOOR AREA	1297 sq. ft.

UNIT 4
LIVING	12' 2" x 14' 10"
KITCHEN	6' 7" x 6' 7"
BED 1	8' 11" x 8' 6"
BED 2	9' 11" x 14' 10"
FLOOR AREA	562 sq. ft.

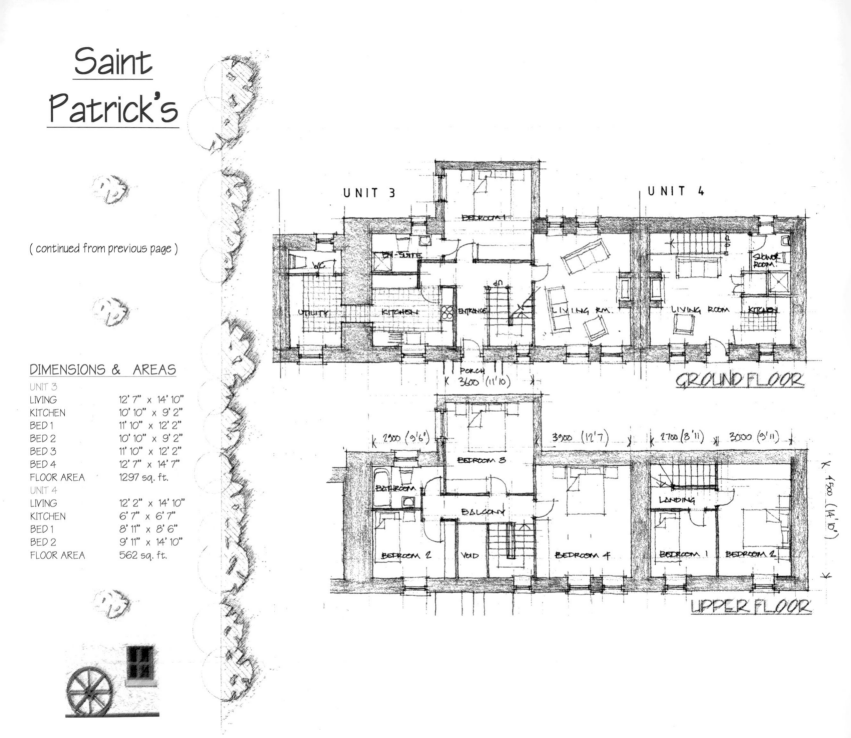

UNIT 3

UNIT 4

BEDROOM 1

WC

EN-SUITE

UTILITY   KITCHEN   ENTRANCE   LIVING RM.   LIVING ROOM   KITCHEN   SHOWER ROOM

UP

PORCH
3600 (11'10)

GROUND FLOOR

2300 (3'6")   3900 (12'7)   2700 (8'11)   3000 (9'11)

BEDROOM 3

BATHROOM

BALCONY

LANDING

1500 (14'0")

BEDROOM 2   VOID   BEDROOM 4   BEDROOM 1   BEDROOM 2

UPPER FLOOR

CONSTRUCTION COST

In an era of constant change and high building inflation it would be futile to suggest an exact construction cost for any specific design shown. However, we have provided below a breakdown of the construction costs which will give a much clearer idea as to amount of financing required at different stages throughout the construction process.

Builders will often quote square foot rate giving an estimated figure, but will use proper costing methods when tendering seriously. The square foot rate varies for each house depending on design, specification, site conditions and finishes. If quoted a square foot rate try to establish from the builder what exactly has been included. The chart below will then help you to establish how much more additional finance is required to complete your project

Chart Group Description

Group A

Based on house on normal site with concrete strip foundations, "3 ft deep", blockwork, concrete ground floor, timber first floor, insulated external cavity walls, timber roof with all roof finishes.

Group B

Normal plastering of house internally and externally with concrete ground floors and timber first floors.
uPVC double glaze windows and external doors with a mid range second fix joinery standard, including for panel doors etc.
Normal plumbing and electrical systems.

Group C

Includes for good quality kitchen, utility, sanitary wear, fireplaces and stairs.
Floor and wall tiling (4 ft high) to all wet areas bathrooms, en-suites, WC's and shower rooms.
All internal paint work to walls and woodwork.

Group D

Modest site works on a normal, flat site, including for a gravel finished drive, a path around house, storm, foul and electrical services completed.

CHART

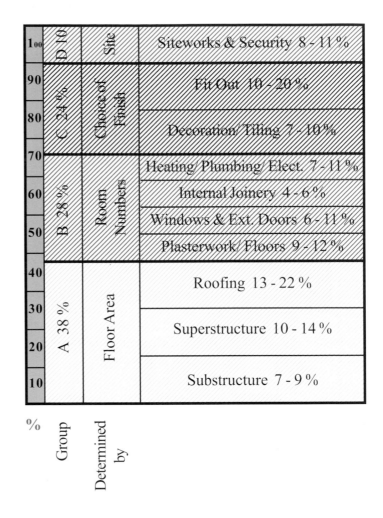

Making your design and budget compatible
Definitely one of the most problematic areas as the two are very rarely compatible. The illusion that reducing the square foot area of a house by say 10% will effect a 10% cost saving is incorrect and unfounded. The second bar of the adjoining chart helps indicate the influencing factors affecting cost, and the following example should help you understand how it works.

Example:
Boundary or retaining walls not included and if required would be additional expense
Professional landscaping
2,000 sq ft house @ £100,000 construction cost, i.e. £50 per sq ft, breaks down as follows:
Group A £38,000
Group B £28,000
Group C £24,000
Group D £10,000
1. A reduction of 10% in the floor area, to 1800 sq ft whilst retaining the same rooms numbers, results in a 10% saving of Group A only, giving a £3,800 saving and not £10,000 as might have been hoped.

2. To achieve a "Pro rata" saving, room numbers and specification and finishes must also be reduced along a similar percentage as the floor area.

You will correctly ascertain from above that a house with small rooms will have a higher Sq ft. rate than it's equal counterpart with larger rooms. Therefore don't make rooms any smaller than you require as it will only give negligible saving now and may cause regret later.

Variables to the chart percentages
The following are scenarios which, are not allowed for and would affect the percentages, indicated on the chart, at different stages.
Group A
Poor site conditions
Excessive "dead building" – from the foundation level to D.P.C. level.
Raft foundations
Stone or brick wall cladding
Intricate roof design
Expensive roof finishes
Group B
Elaborate window design
Excessive windows or external doors
Additional decorative timber work
High quality specification internally
Group C
This almost goes with out saying due to the extensive choice available and also your own desired choice of finish and extra's.
Group D
A service site would result in a saving
A soft low lying site may require filling .
A rocky site may require costly excavation.

Direct Labour
Savings from 5% in the low cost construction regions to 20% in the higher construction cost regions can be obtained by opting for direct labour. But be warned, you have to be prepared to take on a substantial work load and the period for completing your house could easily double due to the present economical climate and demand for labour.

REGIONAL CONSTRUCTION COSTS

As can be seen from the adjoining map, construction costs for similar projects vary greatly throughout the country. The cheapest areas for construction in the northern counties, where as the southern counties and urban area's being the most expensive.
Some of the factors effecting the prices in the lower priced regions are ;
1. High competitiveness resulting in lower profit margins
2. Lower labour rates

The factors effecting prices in the higher regions are the reverse of the above and encouraged by the present high volume of work in the construction industry.

Increase in Regional Construction Costs

15% →   30% →

House Grant (Republic of Ireland)

£3,000 NEW HOUSE GRANT

A grant of £3,000 is available for building or purchasing a new house/flat, provided the house is constructed by a registered contractor, and the floor area does not exceed 1,346 sq.ft. (125 sq.m.). The following conditions may apply:-

a) You or your spouse, either individually or jointly, must never have previously purchased or built for your own occupation another dwelling in Ireland or abroad.
b) You must occupy the dwelling on completion as your normal place of residence.
c) Your application must be received in the Department within a year of occupying the house.
d) The dwelling is new.
e) The dwelling must be built in accordance with good building practice and with the Building Regulations 1991.
f) The dwelling is built by a contractor registered for VAT who holds a current Form C2 or tax clearance certificate. In the case of a house built on an applicant's own site self-build VAT registered work of not less than £ 1 5,000 must be undertaken under contract by the registered contractors.
g) In the case of house located in the Dublin City or County (including the Borough of Dun Laoghaire, but excluding certain largely rural areas of Co. Dublin) it will be necessary that the dwelling has a principal means of space and water heating which uses electricity, gas, oil or a solid fuel burning appliance which will satisfactorily limit smoke emissions. In the addition, an ordinary fireplace which is not the source of water heating for the house and is used solely to heat the room in which it is located is permitted.

In your own interest, you are advised to make an application before work on the house has commenced, or at the time of payment of a deposit, so that a decision on eligibility can be given in good time and a provisional approval issued.

The following documents must accompany the completed application form in any case where the applicant is building (and not purchasing) the house on his own site:-

(i)   Site location map.
(ii)   House plan, elevation and section (scale 1:50).
(iii)   Specification.
(iv)   Planning permission.
(v)   Fire safety certificate (for flats or maisonettes).
In all cases, Form NH2B - certificate from Inspector of Taxes must be submitted with your application.
Applicants may also be required to produce any other documents (e.g. Contract of Sale, evidence of title, etc.) deemed necessary.
In any case where title to the new dwelling is being taken out in the names of two or more persons, details of title including the names of other parties, should be given.

If you are deemed to be eligible for a grant, and the plans and other documents submitted comply with requirements, provisional certificates of approval will be issued to you.

No changes should be made to the approved plans without the prior approval of the Department.

PAYMENT OF GRANT

When the house is finished and occupied, you can claim payment, provided:-

1. All work has been completed in accordance with the approved plans to the Department of the Environments outline specification.
2. You are in occupation of the house as your normal place of residence on a year round basis.

Claim for payment is followed by a final inspection . It may take up to six months before payment is received.

Application for grant must be made on an appropriate form, accompanied by house plans, site location and layout maps, and planning permission, and forwarded to Dept. of Environment in your area.
Head Office, O'Connell Bridge House, Dublin 1.
Telephone (01) 6793377.

FLOOR AREA FOR GRANT PURPOSES

The total floor area of a house for grant purposes must be at least 35 sq.ft. and not more than 125 sq.m. (1 346 sq.ft.). In the case of flats, the maximum is the same (125 sq.m.) with minimum floor area of at least 30 sq.m. These limits are designed to allow the construction of reasonably sized houses and are strictly enforced.

FLOOR AREA CERTIFICATE

Ensure that grant size houses purchased from builders/ developers are accompanied by a floor area certificate (FAC). This ensures that the house is within grant limits, provided that it has been built according to plans. A FAC is also required to obtain exemption from stamp duty on new houses purchased.

SPECIAL EXEMPTIONS

(i) Disabled Persons:-
An exemption to maximum floor area, and on previous ownership can, in some cases be obtained for suitably designed houses for disabled persons. A special application form DP2 should be sought for this type of application.

(ii) Separated Persons:-
An exemption on 'previous ownership' clause may be allowed to separated persons (by order of a court) where refusal to pay a grant would cause undue hardship.

(iii) House Damaged By Fire:-
An exemption on 'previous ownership' clause grants may be allowed where previous house suffered extensive fire/explosion damage, whereby it makes more sense to provide a new house in lieu of repairs to existing.

EXCLUDED AREAS

Fully detached garages, carports and out-offices.
A garage (or carport) attached to, or forming part of a house which complies with the conditions for garages or a single storey, undeveloped garage which is attached to, or forms part of a house, and complies with Dept. regulations. It must also comply with the fire requirements, have provision for not more than two windows, and the entrance must normally be from the front of the house, but consideration will be given in cases where this is not possible due to the restriction of the site. It should not have a fireplace opening or be capable of having a fireplace.

Undeveloped attics which may be floored for storage purposes: Not more than three windows or roof lights, to provide light and ventilation, is also permitted.
Undeveloped basements: Walls must be unplastered internally, and only works necessary to secure the structural stability of the house may be carried out. Separate rooms with external access from the house, may not be provided.
A boiler house/fuel store with external access only, and a floor area of not more than 4 sq.m. (43 sq.ft.)
Small open front porches. Common areas for multi dwelling, buildings.

INCLUDED AREAS

As a general rule you may take it that areas which are capable of being converted into habitable or useful floor space, even if there is not direct access to the rest of the building, and irrespective of the state of finish, will be regarded as part of the floor area.

You are advised to have your plans approved by the Department before you start work, and to check that the dimensions of the house being constructed are in accordance with approved plans, particularly where the floor area is near the maximum limits. This is a brief outline of grant conditions, for further and fully detailed information contact the Department of Environment:
Housing Grant Section, Government Offices, Ballina, Co Mayo, Tel: (096) 70677 and request a copy of HA I Explanatory Memorandum for new House Grants.

Planning Permission (Republic of Ireland)

After choosing your site, and having given some thought as to the nature of the development, the first stage is to apply for planning permission to the Planning Authority in your county, or to the Urban District Council, or in the case of cities, to the City Borough Corporation.

There are three types of planning application which can be made, i.e. outline, approval and full permission, and these are outlined below.

OUTLINE PERMISSION

In some cases, persons may wish to ascertain whether or not planning permission would be granted for a particular development/site. On the advice of your architect/engineer, it may be prudent to apply for outline permission to determine whether or not your development would be permitted. Outline permission allows you to make an application without going to the expense of preparing house plans.

An outline permission must be accompanied by:-
a) Complete application form.
b) Planning fee of £42 per house.
c) Proposed site layout and location maps, showing location of proposed development on site, and giving brief description of same.
d) 2 copies of notice of application to Planning Authority inserted in local newspaper and 2 no. copies site notice.
Note:- Grant of outline permission does not permit carrying out of any works.

APPROVAL

Approval can only be sought where outline permission as described above, has already been granted, and must be accompanied by complete working drawings and specification, together with all documents as listed for outline permission. Planning fee per house - £21.00.
Note:- If Approval is granted after outline permission has previously been sought and granted, the duration of Approval runs from the date of granting of Outline Permission.

FULL PERMISSION

Full permission is a combination of outline and approval as previously described and is a more direct and speedier method for sites where it is considered that planning permission should be relatively easy to obtain.

GENERAL PROCEDURE

Should the Planning Authority decide that insufficient information has been supplied they are entitled to request further information, whereby, the three months processing period commences only after they have received a full reply to the further information requested. Therefore, in some cases, incomplete or awkward applications can take longer. An application for outline permission followed by approval, takes twice as long as an initial application for full permission. In all cases when a decision is made, the applicant is notified within two months of a decision to grant, or refuse, the permission applied for, provided there is no objection to same, the planning approval is issued one month later.

PUBLIC NOTICE

This is done by means of a newspaper notice in a locally distributed newspaper and also with a notice on site placed in a convenient position so as to be legible from main thoroughfare, and must remain in place for the duration of the application. 2 no. copies of each to be submitted with application for planning.

SITE LAYOUT MAPS

4 no. layout maps, showing clearly boundaries of the site, site entrance, storm and foul drainage details, water supply etc., Letter of consent from any group schemes or landowners to right-of-ways, etc., to accompany application. Proven site lines also required to be shown on map.

SITE LOCATION MAPS

4 no. site location maps, being extracts from Ordnance Survey sheets, and showing clearly the location of site and adjoining developments in relation to any churches, crossroads, towns, etc., or any other distinct landmark in the area. Outline of site to be marked in red and overall landowners holding outlined in blue.

HOUSE PLANS

4 no. copies of detailed plans and specifications, clearly illustrating layout, elevations, sections, details of finishes, and all materials, etc., to be used in the construction.
Note:- These need not accompany outline permission.

OBJECTION

Objection can be made in writing as follows:-
a) By the applicant to the Planning Authority in relation to it's decision to refuse, or to object to some of the conditions relevant to the Grant of Permission. The applicant has one month from the date of receipt of a decision, within which to object.
b) Objections can be lodged by a third party against a planning application, and if an objection is made, the objector is notified of the Councils decision, at which stage he has a further 21 days to appeal the Council's decision. Further details of fees will be outlined on the Planning Authority's Decision to Grant Permission form.

Details of complete documents required for planning applications, as follows:-
a) Complete application form, completed accurately, stating all details as requested.
b) Completed application Fee form, with remittance
c) 4 no. copies of plans, elevations, site maps, site location maps and 2 no. copies of newspaper notice, site notice and letter from Group Scheme if applicable.

This information is a simple guide. It is advisable to contact your local Planning Office who will be glad to assist you with full relevant information concerning your application.

Concepts for Irish Homes
(Revised and Reprinted)

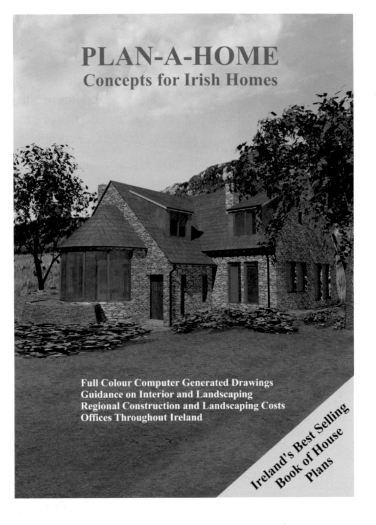

Currently the **BEST SELLING** book of house plans in Ireland having **SOLD OUT** inside a year.
If you don't already own a copy you can order it today **LoCALL 1890 222345**
Or dial 00 353 74 29651 (outside Eire).Priced £11.99 (P & P free within Ireland)
Also available from all good book shops. Priced £11.99

ORDER FORM

This form is to be used for direct ordering of unaltered plans. (For altered plans see page 5)

PHONE 1890 222345 FOR PLAN COSTS *(00 353 74 29651 outside Eire)*

Design No.

Planning/Working Drawings	£
(8 sets of plans & 4 sets of specification)	
Reverse hand layout £60.00 extra.	£
Bill of quantities (Optional)	£
Total	£
Vat @ 21%	£
Total Due	£

Name: _____

Address: _____

Tel. No: _____

Site Address: _____

_____

_____

Other Items required for planning permission:

4 sets of site layout/location map.
2 copies of site notice.
2 copies of newspaper notice.
Fully completed application form.
Planning application fee.
Percolation test (dependent on Local Authority)

Payment Details:

Cheque ☐

Postal Order ☐

Visa ☐

Account No:

Expiry Date:

Cardholders Signature:

Please post to:

PLAN-A-HOME
Lower Main Street,
Letterkenny,
Co. Donegal.
Ireland.

Should you require any assistance contact any of the appointed Architectural offices listed inside on the back cover.

Please complete your Specification list over leaf.

Customer Specification

Please tick the following to enable us to complete a detailed specification to suit your requirements, (otherwise we shall allow for a good quality, standard finish throughout).

Floor Construction

Ground :
- Concrete ☐
- Suspended Timber ☐
- Hollowcore ☐

First :
- Timber Joists ☐
- T Beams ☐
- Hollowcore ☐

Roof Covering

Tiles - Concrete ☐
Clay ☐
Slates - Synthetic ☐
Natural ☐

Other _____

Windows

- Hardwood ☐
- uPVC ☐
- Aluminium ☐
- Other _____

External Doors/Frames

- Hardwood ☐
- uPVC ☐
- Aluminium ☐
- Other _____

External Finish

- Dry Dash ☐
- Wet Dash ☐
- Smooth Render ☐
- Brick ☐
- Stone ☐

Wall Insulation

- Standard Cavity Insulation ☐
- Dry Lining ☐
- Other _____

Stairs

- Hardwood throughout ☐
- Hardwood sides, carpeted ☐
- Standard Red Deal ☐

Dormer Finish

- Render ☐
- uPVC ☐
- Slate ☐
- Lead ☐
- Other _____

Fascia, Soffit & Barge

- Softwood ☐
- Hardwood ☐
- Aluminium ☐
- uPVC ☐
- Colour _____

Gutters

- Aluminium ☐
- uPVC ☐
- Other _____

Second-Fix Joinery

- Sapelle Doors ☐
- Raise Panel Doors ☐
- Hardwood Panel Doors ☐
- Other _____

Second-Fix Joinery Timbers

- Softwood ☐
- Hardwood ☐
- MDF ☐
- Other _____

Garage Door

- Hardwood ☐
- Overhead & Insulated ☐
- Roller Shutter ☐
- Remote Control ☐
- Other _____

Room Ventilation

- Wall Vents ☐
- Window Trickle Vents ☐

Heating

- Oil ☐
- Gas ☐
- Electric ☐
- Solid Fuel ☐
- Other ☐

Do You Require Any Of The Following?
(Please indicate which room)

'Irish Oak' Flooring to _____
Timber ceilings to _____
Ornate Plaster Coving to _____
Gas Fires to _____

Floor Tiling to _____
Gypsum Ceiling Coving to _____
Glazed Internal Doors to _____
Radon Barrier to _____
Central Cleaning system _____

Any Other Requirements

_____
_____
_____

144